CONTENTS

Book 1.1

DAY BY DAY

TOGETHER IS BETTER

WITHDRAWN

McGraw-Hill School Division

STORIES TO TELL

LET'S FIND OUT!

McGraw-Hill School Division

UNIT 1: THINK ABOUT IT!

McGraw-Hill School Division

UNIT 2: MANY PATHS

Name______________________ Date__________ **Practice 1**

Short *a*

Say each word and write it on the line.
Then circle the picture it names.

1. mat ____________

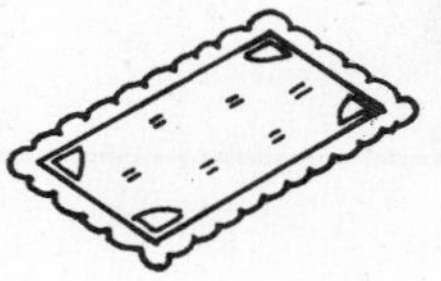 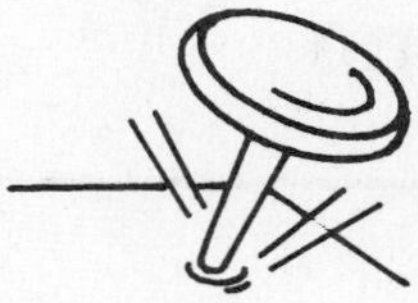

2. cap ____________

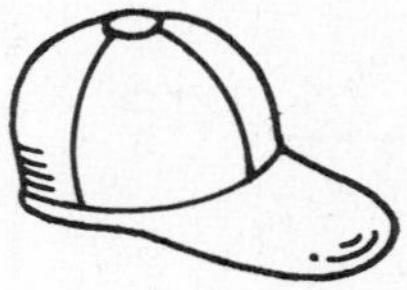 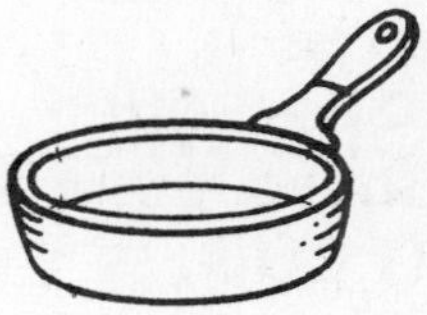

3. cat ____________

 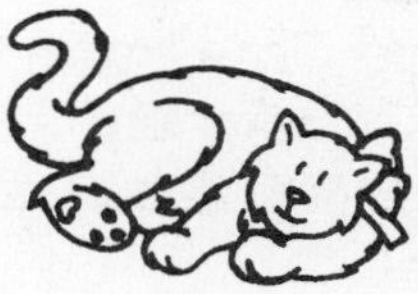

4. ham ____________

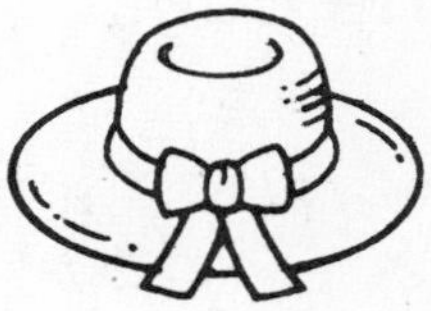 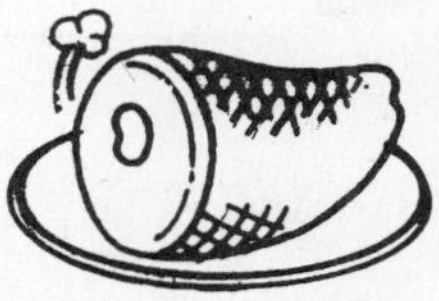

5. bat ____________

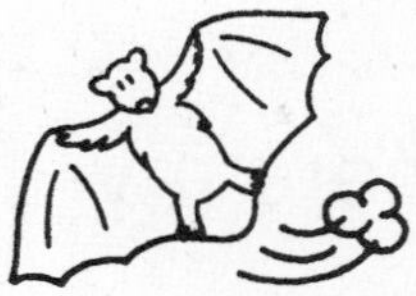 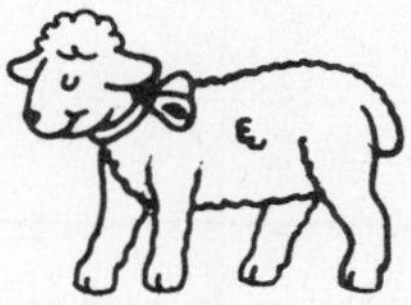

6. van ____________

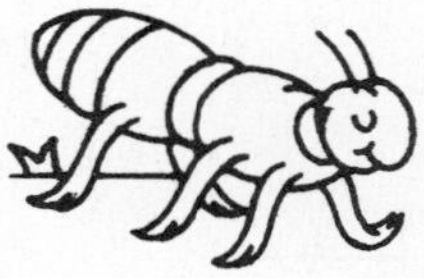 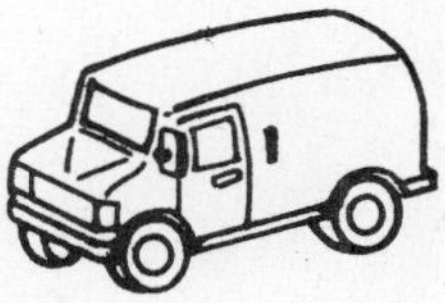

At Home: Have children choose a favorite word from the exercise and use it in a sentence.

High-Frequency Words

Write the word from the box that fits in each sentence.
Circle the picture that goes with the sentence.

one	give	this	likes

1. She will _____ me a cap.

2. He _____ the cat.

3. _____ is where my dog has a nap.

4. We have _____ car.

At Home: Have children choose a picture and write another
sentence to go with it.

Book 1.1
Max, the Cat

4

McGraw-Hill School Division

Ham, Jam, and One Yam

Yes, Pam can give Sam one yam. Sam can give Pam ham and jam.

Now the cat has ham and jam. The cat likes Pam!

Now the bat has one yam. The bat likes Sam!

At Home: Encourage children to talk about a time when they wanted something but could not have it. How did that make them feel?

4

2a

This cat is mad. Pam wants to give the cat one yam. But the cat likes ham with jam. Pam has no ham with jam. That is bad. The cat is sad.

This bat is mad. Sam wants to give the bat ham with jam. But the bat likes yams. Sam does not have yams.

Sam runs to Pam. Can Pam give Sam one yam?

Story Comprehension

Read each sentence.
Write **T** if the sentence is true.
Write **F** if the sentence is false.

1. _____ Max is a cat.

2. _____ Pam has a cap.

3. _____ Pam has a cat.

4. _____ Max likes to nap on the mat.

5. _____ Pam likes to nap in the cap.

6. _____ Pam is mad and sad.

At Home: Have children write a sentence explaining why
Pam and Max got mad at each other.

Parts of a Book

Book Cover

Title

Author

Picture

Title Page

Title

Author

Use the **book cover** and the **title page** to answer these questions.

1. What is on the cover of the book?

_____

- - - - - - - - - - - - - - - - - - -

_____

2. What is the title of the book?

_____

- - - - - - - - - - - - - - - - - - -

_____

3. Who wrote the book?

_____

- - - - - - - - - - - - -

_____

4. Who is Pam?

_____

- - - - - - - - - - - - -

_____

At Home: Have children point to the title of the book and the author's name.

McGraw-Hill School Division

Short *a*

Circle the word that names each picture.
Then write the word.

1.

cap   bat

_____

- - - - - - - - -

_____

2.

tag   cat

_____

- - - - - - - - -

_____

3.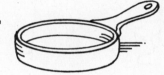

can   pan

_____

- - - - - - - - -

_____

4.

hat   ham

_____

- - - - - - - - -

_____

5.

rag   bag

_____

- - - - - - - - -

_____

6.

fan   man

_____

- - - - - - - - -

_____

6 Book 1.1
Max, the Cat

At Home: Have children use some of the words they
wrote in sentences.

Short *a*; Consonants

Sound out each word.
Write the word on the line.
Then circle the picture that it describes.

1. j a m

_____

- - - - - - -

_____

2. b a g

_____

- - - - - - -

_____

3. p a n

_____

- - - - - - -

_____

  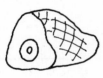

4. r a g

_____

- - - - - - -

_____

At Home: Have children make up sentences using the words.

Book 1.1
Max, the Cat 4

Use Illustrations

Circle the picture on the right that belongs with
the picture on the left.

1.

2.

3.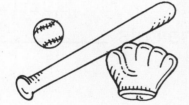

4.

5.

At Home: Have children write a sentence using one of the
picture pairs.

Inflectional Ending *-s*

Add **-s** to tell what one person or thing does.

Circle the word that completes the sentence.
Then write the word on the line.

1. Sam _____ in the van.

   nap   naps

2. They _____ the cat.

   pat   pats

3. The pup _____ his tail.

   wag   wags

4. The cats _____.

   nap   naps

5. Dan _____ me.

   tag   tags

6. Pat _____ the can.

   tap   taps

McGraw-Hill School Division

At Home: Ask children to draw a picture that illustrates one of the sentences.

Digraph *ck*

Change the last letter of each word to **ck**.
Write the new word under the picture that it names.

1. pat

_____

— — — — — — — — — —

_____

2. sat

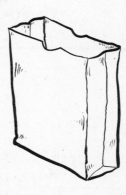

_____

— — — — — — — — — —

_____

3. bat

_____

— — — — — — — — — —

_____

4. tap

_____

— — — — — — — — — —

_____

McGraw-Hill School Division

4 Book 1.1
Quack

At Home: Have children change the last letter of **sad** to
ck. Then have them draw a picture of the new word.

High-Frequency Words

Write the correct word in the space.
Then fill in the crossword puzzle.

on	they	what	your

Across

_____

2. _____ are happy.

_____

4. My cap is _____ Pam.

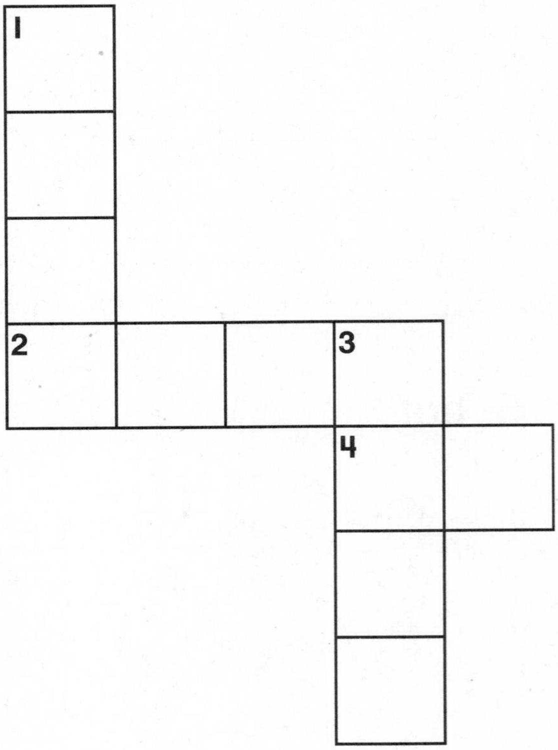

Down

_____

1. _____ is in the sack?

_____

3. I have _____ map.

At Home: Invite children to make a word search puzzle
using the four words in the box.

McGraw-Hill School Division

The Duck Shack

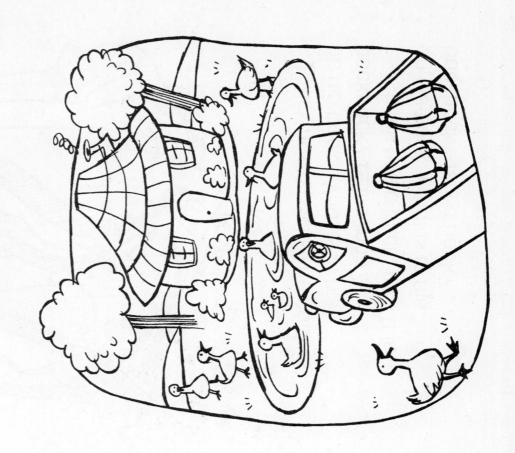

"What is in your pack?" I ask
Jack. "What is in your pack,
Chuck?"

Quack! Quack!
There are ducks in the packs!
Jack and Chuck take the ducks
in a truck to a duck shack!

At Home: Invite children to play a game in which they hide something in a pack or bag and take turns guessing what is inside.

4

10a

Jack has a pack. The pack is on his back. What is in his backpack? Is it a map?

Chuck has a pack, too. It is on his back. What is in his backpack? Is it a book?

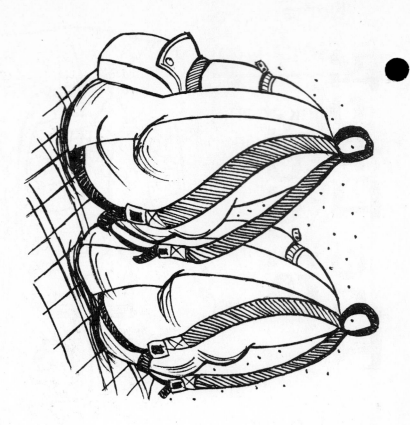

They do not have a map. They do not have a book. Do they have a lock? Do they have sticks? No, they do not have a lock. They do not have sticks.

Story Comprehension

Think about the story "Quack."
Then circle the right answer to finish each sentence.

1. Dad and Nan ___.

  a. nap

  b. pack

  c. swim

2. They put things in a ___.

  a. van

  b. ship

  c. cab

3. Jack and Mack ___.

  a. tap

  b. are mad

  c. help Dad

4. Nan packs her ___.

  a. bat

  b. cat

  c. bag

5. Jack hears a ___.

  a. quack, quack

  b. bark, bark

  c. moo, moo

6. Nan has a pet ___.

  a. cat

  b. duck

  c. cow

At Home: Have children draw a picture of their favorite
part of the story. Then ask them to write a sentence
about it.

Parts of a Book

The **author** of a book writes the story. The **illustrator** makes the pictures.

Author

The Jam Man

By Max Bag
Illustrated by Sam Tack

Illustrator

Look at the book cover on this page.

1. Who is the author?

_____

- - - - - - - - - - - - - - - - - - -

_____

2. What is the name of the illustrator?

_____

- - - - - - - - - - - - - - - - - - -

_____

3. What does the author do?

_____

- - - - - - - - - - - - - - - - - - -

_____

4. What does the illustrator do?

_____

- - - - - - - - - - - - - - - - - - -

_____

At Home: Have children describe the picture on the book cover.

12

Book 1.1
Quack   4

McGraw-Hill School Division

Digraph *ck*

Use these words to answer the riddles.

back	pack	quack	sack	rack

1. A duck does this.

_____

- - - - - - - - - - -

_____

2. I am not the front.

_____

- - - - - - - - - - -

_____

3. You carry things in me.
What am I?

_____

- - - - - - - - - - -

_____

4. I go on top of a car.

_____

- - - - - - - - - - -

_____

5. You do this for a trip.

_____

- - - - - - - - - - -

_____

5 Book 1.1
Quack

At Home: Have children make up a riddle for *tack*.

13

Short *a; ck*

Circle the word that describes each picture.
Write the word.

1.

pack

nap

_____

- - - - - -

_____

2.

back

bat

_____

- - - - - -

_____

3.

rack

van

_____

- - - - - -

_____

4.

sack

tap

_____

- - - - - -

_____

5.

quack

wag

_____

- - - - - -

_____

6.

tack

cap

_____

- - - - - -

_____

At Home: Have children draw a picture of one of the words they did not circle.

Sequence of Events

Number the pictures **1**, **2**, **3** to show what happened first, next, and last.
The first one is done for you.

3   **1**   **2**

1.

_____   _____   _____

2.

_____   _____   _____

2 | Book 1.1
Quack

At Home: Have children draw a picture of something that could happen next for each row.

Inflectional Ending -s

Add **-s** to tell what one person or thing does.

Add an **-s** to the underlined word.
Then write the new word to tell what one person or thing does.

1. The ducks <u>quack</u>.

_____

- - - - - - - -

The duck _____.

2. Mack and Jan <u>pat</u> the cat.

_____

- - - - - - -

Mack _____ the cat.

3. Jack and Mack <u>tack</u> the map.

_____

- - - - - - - -

Jack _____ the map.

4. Pam and Sam <u>nap</u> on the mat.

_____

- - - - - - -

Sam _____ on the mat.

At Home: Help children to write another sentence using one of the verbs.

Book 1.1
Quack

4

McGraw-Hill School Division

Short *i*

Write a word from the box to finish the sentence.

hid	wig	dig	pig	lid	kick

1. I have a big _____.

2. Pam likes her _____.

3. Max _____ his bib.

4. The _____ is on the pan.

5. I _____ in it.

6. I can _____ it.

6 Book 1.1
What Does Pig Do?

At Home: Have children write one more sentence using a word from the box.

17

McGraw-Hill School Division

High-Frequency Words

Write words from the box to finish the letter to Nick.

does	her	look	there

Dear Nick,

What _____ your cat like to do?

Can you take _____ to the cat show?

Did you ever go _____ with your cat?

You can _____ at the cats that go there.

Your friend,

Tim

At Home: Have children write a sentence using one of the words in the box.

Book 1.1
What Does Pig Do? 4

Fish Sisters

But Kim's skin does look like Mindy's skin. Her big fins look like Mindy's fins.
So Kim does look like her sister Mindy!

At Home: Have children talk about ways in which they resemble family members and friends.

4

18a

2

Does Kim the fish look like her sister Mindy? There are ways to see.
Mindy is big. Is Kim?
Mindy is thick. Is Kim?

What Does Pig Do? McGraw-Hill School Division

Kim is not big. Kim is not thick. She is as little as a stick. So Kim does not look like her sister.

3

18b

Story Comprehension

Write what Pig does on each of the days.

Pig kicks.	Pig taps.
Pig does laps.	Pig digs.
Pig bats.	

1. Tuesday:		_____ _____
2. Wednesday:		_____ _____
3. Thursday:		_____ _____
4. Friday:		_____ _____
5. Saturday:		_____ _____

5   Book 1.1
What Does Pig Do?

At Home: Have children draw a picture of themselves doing one of the activities that Pig does.

19

Parts of a Book

You can find what is in a book in the **table of contents**.

Table of Contents

Nick's Dip. 3

Rick Tags a Pig 7

One Sad Duck 10

The Man With a Map. 12

Read the table of contents.

1. On what page does **The Man With a Map** begin?

_____

- - - - - - - - - - - - - - - - - - - -

_____

2. On what page does **Nick's Dip** begin?

_____

- - - - - - - - - - - - - - - - - - - -

_____

3. What story begins on page 10?

_____

- - - - - - - - - - - - - - - - - - - -

_____

4. What story begins on page 7?

_____

- - - - - - - - - - - - - - - - - - - -

_____

At Home: Have children look at other examples of tables of contents.

Book 1.1
What Does Pig Do? 4

20

Short *i*

Write the letter **i** to complete each word.
Then draw a line between the completed
word and its picture.

1. p _____ g

2. s _____ x

3. w _____ g

4. d _____ g

5. b _____ b

6. k _____ ck

At Home: Have children pronounce each of the words
they completed. Make sure they note that each word has
the short *i* sound.

21

Short *i, a; ck*

Look at the pictures.
Read the word choices.
Print the two words that describe each picture.

I.

lick	sick		pig	dig

2.

big	wig		kick	quick

3.

zip	lip		bag	tag

4.

sad	glad		cat	bat

At Home: Have children list other words that contain the
short **a**, short **i**, or **-ck** sounds.

Book 1.1
What Does Pig Do?   4

McGraw-Hill School Division

Sequence of Events

Number the sentences below to show the order in which things happen.

Dan wants to pat his cat.

_____

_____ The cat sits in Dan's lap.

_____

_____ Dan sits.

_____

_____ Dan pats the cat in his lap.

Pam wants ham.

_____

_____ Pam ran to the store.

_____

_____ Pam eats the ham.

_____

_____ Pam gets a ham in a bag.

6 | Book 1.1
What Does Pig Do?

At Home: Have children tell what might be the next step in each of the above sequences.

23

McGraw-Hill School Division

Context Clues

If you don't know what a word means, look at the other words around it for clues.

Write the word in the sentence that helps tell the meaning of the underlined word.

1. A <u>cap</u> is a hat. _____

2. The sick man is very <u>ill</u>. _____

3. That <u>sack</u> is a big bag. _____

4. Jim and Nick dance a <u>jig</u>. _____

At Home: Have children choose one of the underlined words from the sentences above and draw a picture to show its meaning.

Book 1.1
What Does Pig Do?
4

McGraw-Hill School Division

Digraphs *sh, th*

Complete the sentences.
Then circle the letters that stand for the sound of **sh**
or **th** in each word.

| wish | ship | bath | thin | thick |

1. We are on a _____.

2. A cat can be fat or _____.

3. I can _____ on a star.

4. Pam is taking a _____.

5. Our dog has _____ hair.

High-Frequency Words

Write the word that completes each sentence.
Circle the picture that goes with the sentence.

be	could	down	see

1. The man ran

_____

_____ the path.

3. The cat likes to

_____

_____ fat.

_____

2. I can _____
the map.

_____

4. _____
I have that hat?

At Home: Have children make up a new question for one of
the words.

Book 1.1
The Path on the Map   4

McGraw-Hill School Division

Pig's Wish

"Shells!" said Cat. And soon
Pig had her wish.
"I am glad I asked Cat for
help!" said Pig. She was glad.
She had a big seashell home.

At Home: Invite children to recall a time they helped
a friend make something. What did they make? Did
they have fun making it?

4

One day Pig went down to see Cat. Pig wanted to see if she could be Cat's helper.

"Hi, Cat," said Pig. "Can you help me make a home?" Cat said, "Yes."

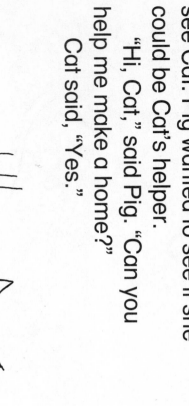

Pig and Cat went to look for rocks and sticks. There were none.

"How will I make a home?" asked Pig.

Story Comprehension

Circle the sentences that tell what happens to the characters in "The Path on the Map."

I. They see cats in the shack.

2. They see a cow on the map.

3. They see a shack on the map.

4. They see some fish in the shack.

5. They see a pig on the map.

6. They see a bat on the map.

7. They see a duck on the map.

8. They see a van on the map.

9. They see a fish on the map.

McGraw-Hill School Division

9 Book 1.1
The Path on the Map

At Home: Have children number the events they circled in the order in which they happened in the story.

27

Parts of a Book

A **picture dictionary** lists words in A-B-C order.
Each word has a picture that goes with it.

Look at the page from a picture dictionary.
Write the answer on the line.

1. What word comes after **on**?

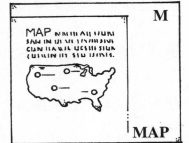

_____

_____

2. What word comes before **on**?

_____

_____

3. What word is a kind of animal?

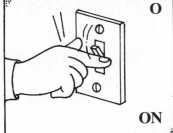

_____

_____

4. What is the first word?

_____

_____

McGraw-Hill School Division

At Home: Have children make picture-dictionary drawings
for a few other animal words.

Book 1.1
The Path on the Map 4

Digraphs *sh, th*

Write the name of each picture from the list of words.
Then circle the letters in each word that stand for
the sound of **sh** or **th**.

| bath | path | fish | thin | ship | shape |

1.

_____

- - - - - - - - - - - -

_____

2.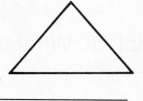

_____

- - - - - - - - - - - -

_____

3.

_____

- - - - - - - - - - - -

_____

4.

_____

- - - - - - - - - - - -

_____

5.

_____

- - - - - - - - - - - -

_____

6.

_____

- - - - - - - - - - - -

_____

6 Book 1.1
The Path on the Map

At Home: Have children write **wish** at the top of a piece of
paper. Have them write a list of things they wish for.

29

sh, th, ck; Short *i, a*

Use the words in the box to answer the riddles.
The pictures are clues.

thin	big	fish	sack

1. I am not small. What am I?

_____

- - - - - - - -

_____

2. I am like a bag. What am I?

_____

- - - - - - - -

_____

3. I have fins. What am I?

_____

- - - - - - - -

_____

4. I am not fat. What am I?

_____

- - - - - - - -

_____

At Home: Have students make up a clue that describes the
word **cat.**

Book 1.1
The Path on the Map
4

McGraw-Hill School Division

Use Illustrations

Circle the picture that shows what each person needs.

1.

2.

 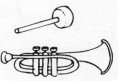

3.

4.

4 Book 1.1
The Path on the Map

At Home: Invite children to tell a story about one of the pictures.

Context Clues

Words or pictures surrounding a word can help you
to understand what that word means.

Write the word that tells about the picture.

1.

pack   shack

_____

- - - - - - - - - - -

_____

2.

mash   map

_____

- - - - - - - - - - -

_____

3.

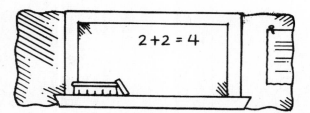

path   math

_____

- - - - - - - - - - -

_____

4.

wish   fish

_____

- - - - - - - - - - -

_____

At Home: Have children illustrate one of the words that is
not pictured on this page.

sh, th, ck; Short *i, a*

Add the correct letter or letters to complete each picture name.

a	i	sh	th	ck

1.

_____

- - - -

pa _____

2.

- - - -

w _____ g

3.

_____

- - - -

fi _____

4.

_____

- - - -

pa _____

5.

_____

- - - -

c _____ t

6.

_____

- - - -

d _____ g

6 Book 1.1
Ships

At Home: Have children pronounce each of the words they completed on this page.

33

High-Frequency Words

Write the word from the list that completes each sentence.

look	this	one	what

1. Look at _____ fan!

2. Did you _____ at his hat?

3. _____ is this?

4. We have _____ big cat and two small cats.

At Home: Have children look through a book and find a sentence that uses one of the words in the box.

Book 1.1
Ships 4

McGraw-Hill School Division

A Path to the Ships

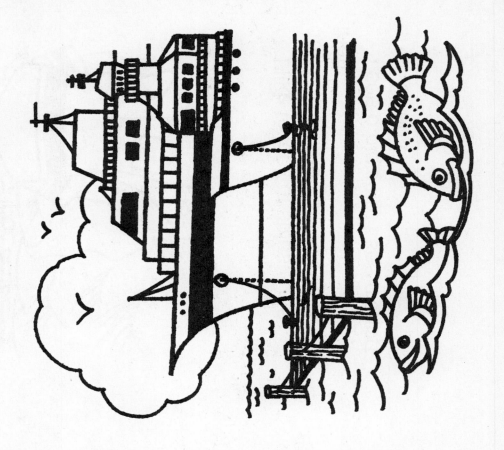

But what I see now is one big fish!
I am not sad I am here. Fish and ships are fun to look at! I am glad.

4

I like to look at ships. One day I go on the path to see them.

I see a big ship. I see a short ship. Or do I?

Ships McGraw-Hill School Division

What kind of ship is that? It is thick. It goes splash.

I want to look at this ship some more.

Story Comprehension

Some names for ships are below.
Circle the ones that were in "Ships."
Then write the names of the ships next to the
pictures.

1. big ship   **2.** little ship   **3.** Navy ship

4. her ship   **5.** steam ship   **6.** toy ship

7.  _____

8. _____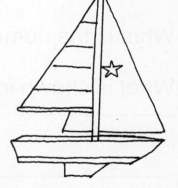

9. 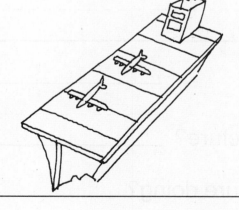 _____

10. _____

At Home: Have children write a sentence telling which
ship is their favorite and why.

Parts of a Magazine

Look at the word and picture on the **magazine** cover. Then answer the questions.

_____

- - - - - - - - - - - - - - - - - - -

1. What is the name of the magazine? _____

2. What is shown in the picture on the cover?

_____

- -

_____

_____

- - - - - - - - - - - - - - - - - - -

3. How many cats are in the picture? _____

4. What are the cats in the picture doing?

_____

- -

_____

At Home: Have children draw cover illustrations for a magazine about birds.

Book 1.1
Ships!
4

McGraw-Hill School Division

Use Illustrations

Underline the sentence that tells about the picture.

1.

The cat sat on a mat.

The cat sat on a hat.

2.

I have a new wig.

I have a new van.

3.

The bib has a rip.

The bag has a rip.

4.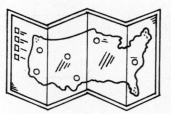

Dan has a map.

Dan has a fan.

5.

The duck ran.

The duck has a nap.

5 Book 1.1
Ships

At Home: Have children find a picture in a storybook and write one sentence about the picture.

37

Sequence of Events

Write **1**, **2**, or **3** to show the order in which things take place.

_____ _____ _____

- -

1. _____ _____ _____

 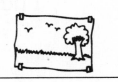 

_____ _____ _____

- -

2. _____ _____ _____

_____ _____ _____

- -

3. _____ _____ _____

  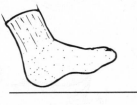

_____ _____ _____

- -

4. _____ _____ _____

At Home: Ask children to draw a picture that shows what could come next in one of the sequences above.

Book 1.1
Ships /4

McGraw-Hill School Division

Inflectional Ending -*s*

Add -**s** to tell what one person or thing does.

Write the word that completes the sentence.

1. The kid _____ up sticks.

   pick   picks

2. Max and Sam _____ into the cab.

   jam   jams

3. The man _____ a path.

   map   maps

4. My cats _____ at my chin!

   nips   nip

5. Jan _____ her bag.

   pack   packs

At Home: Choose two sentences with children and draw new pictures to illustrate them.

McGraw-Hill School Division

Context Clues

You can sometimes find out the meaning of a word by looking at the words or pictures surrounding it.

Write the word that helps tell the meaning of the underlined word.

1. The quick duck had to <u>dash</u>.

2. I sip the <u>drink</u>.

3. I will hit the ball when I <u>bat</u>.

4. This <u>cap</u> is like my hat.

5. We <u>pay</u> with cash.

At Home: Have children write a new sentence for one of the words they wrote down.

McGraw-Hill School Division

High-Frequency Words Review

Circle the word that completes each sentence.

1. _____ you go?

   Could

   Jam

2. Jack _____ quick.

   and

   be

3. _____ do you see?

   They

   What

4. _____ the ship tip?

   Does

   Tag

5. The van is _____ .

   cat

   there

6. He was _____ big.

   this

   bat

7. Can you _____ it?

   see

   Sam

8. Take _____ bath!

   math

   your

8 | Book 1.1
High-Frequency Words Review

At Home: Have children make up another sentence for each of the words they circled.

41

High-Frequency Words Review

Circle the word that tells about the picture.

1.

jam

one

2.

pack

look

3.

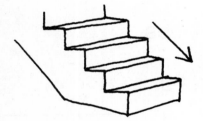

down

up

4.

her

him

5.

I

they

6.

hat

give

At Home: Have children choose one of the words they circled and make up a sentence using that word.

McGraw-Hill School Division

Short *u*

Write the word that names each picture.

pup	mug	tub	duck	bus	fun

1.  _____

2.  _____

3.  _____

4.  _____

5.  _____

6.  _____

6 Book 1.2
One Good Pup

At Home: Help children to make up rhymes using words that have the short *u* sound.

43

McGraw-Hill School Division

High-Frequency Words

Write a word from the box to complete each sentence.
Circle the picture that goes with the sentence.

no	ride	small	out

1. We go for a _____ .

2. Max said, "_____ cats!"

3. That ship is _____ .

4. I want to go _____ .

 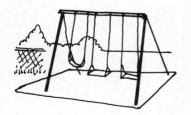

At Home: Have children use each high-frequency word in another sentence.

Book 1.2
One Good Pup 4

Fun in the Sun

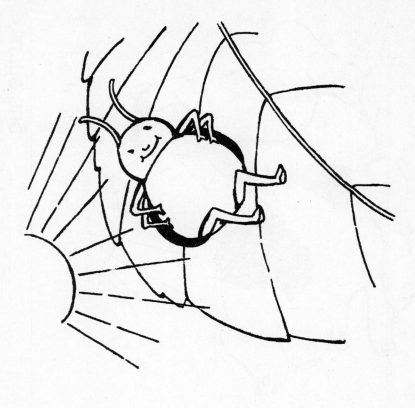

The rug is in the sun. That is fun. The bug likes the sun. Now the pup is back from the tub. The pup and the bug can run in the sun!

At Home: Have children talk about how different kinds of animals interact with each other.

4

A pup dug in the mud. It was fun.

A small bug was in the mud. She got on the pup to go for a ride.

"This pup can be my bus," said the bug.

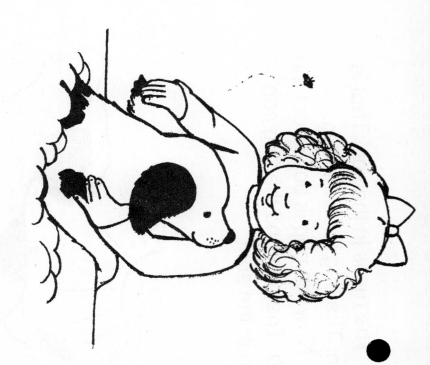

The pup ran out of the mud. The pup ran to a tub. No, the bug will not go to the tub. The bug will go in the rug. The pup will get a scrub. Then he will get a hug.

Story Comprehension

Circle the sentences that tell what happened in "One Good Pup."

1. The pup wants to go out.

2. It is a wet day.

3. The boy and the pup run in the sun.

4. The boy and the pup sit in a ship.

5. They go with dad in the van.

6. The boy and the pup play tug.

7. They fish in the tub.

8. The pup is good.

8 Book 1. 2
One Good Pup

At Home: Ask children to illustrate one of the sentences they circled.

45

McGraw-Hill School Division

A Map

This **picture map** shows the inside of a school.

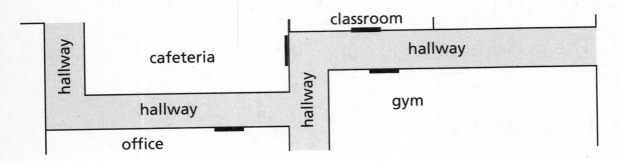

Answer the questions.

1. Which room is next to the cafeteria?

_____

- - - - - - - - - - - - - - - - - - - -

_____

2. How many hallways are there?

_____

- - - - - - - - - - - - - - - - - - - -

_____

3. Where would you go to play games?

_____

- - - - - - - - - - - - - - - - - - - -

_____

4. Is the office at the top or bottom of the map?

_____

- - - - - - - - - - - - - - - - - - - -

_____

At Home: Have children draw a map of several objects in a yard, a park, or a schoolyard.

46

Book 1.2
One Good Pup 4

Short *u*

Look at the pictures.
Read the words.
Then write the two words that tell about the picture.

1. bug   hug   jug

_____   _____

_____ in a _____

2. cut   nut   hut

_____   _____

_____ the _____

3. duck   muck   tuck

_____   _____

_____ in the _____

4. bun   run   sun

_____   _____

_____ on the _____

McGraw-Hill School Division

At Home: Play a riddle game with children to help them identify words with the short **u** sound. For instance, "I'm thinking of something that shines on us and is very hot. What is it?" (sun)

Short *u, i, a; sh, th*

Choose the word that completes the sentence.
Use the picture as a clue.
Then write the word.

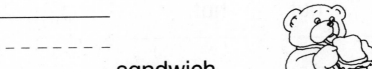

| ship | duck | bath | thick | pig | rush |

1. The _____ is in the mud.

2. This is a _____ sandwich.

3. The _____ said "quack."

4. I can see a _____.

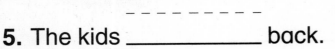

5. The kids _____ back.

6. The cat sits in the _____.

At Home: Challenge children to use as many of these words
as they can in a single sentence: **ant, wish, with, hut**.

Book 1.2
One Good Pup   6

McGraw-Hill School Division

Story Elements

Read the story.
Then answer the questions.

A boy and his pup want to go out. It is too wet! So the boy and his pup nap. Then they fish in the tub. They also ride on a wagon.
The boy tells the pup he is a good dog.

CHARACTER

1. Who is the story about?

PLOT

2. What happens first?

3. What happens next?

4. How does the story end?

4 Book 1.2
One Good Pup

At Home: Ask children what else the boy and his pup might do together while it is raining outside.

49

Inflectional Ending *-ed*

Add **-ed** to a word to tell what someone or something did.

Draw a line to the word that completes the sentence.

1. Sam _____ the bag.   wished

   Mack _____ he was a fox.   packed

2. Grandma _____ Max into bed.   tucked

   The cat _____ the dish.   licked

3. Dick _____ a pet.   rushed

   Kim _____ to the hut.   picked

4. Max _____ the plums into jam.   mashed

   Jan _____ the shack.   locked

McGraw-Hill School Division

At Home: Ask children to draw pictures for two sentences on this page.

Short *o*

Sound out and say each word.
Print the word on the line.
Then circle the picture it names.

1. h o t _____

2. r o c k _____

3. b o x _____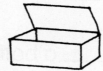

4. h o p _____

4 Book 1. 2
The Bug Bath

At Home: Have children use the words they wrote in sentences.

51

High-Frequency Words

Write a word from the box to complete each sentence.

want	saw	two	very

_____

- - - - - - - - - -

1. The bugs _____ the tub.

_____

- - - - - - - - - -

2. The water was _____ hot.

_____

- - - - - - - - - -

3. "We _____ a bath," said the bugs.

_____

- - - - - - - - - -

4. The _____ bugs got in.

At Home: Ask children to make up a sentence using each of the vocabulary words.

Book 1.2
The Bug Bath   4

McGraw-Hill School Division

Hot Pot

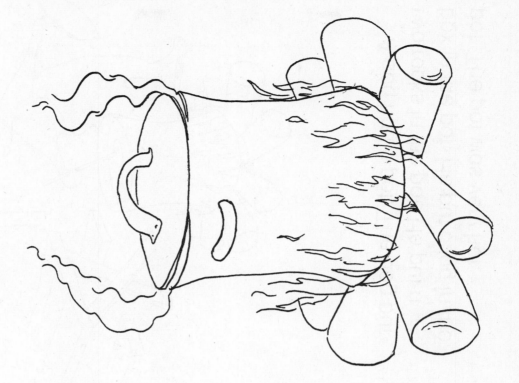

The hogs ran and got the pot.
"Ow!" said the hogs. "This pot is very hot!"
Now the hogs did not like the pot. So they gave the pot back to the dog.

At Home: Encourage children to talk about a time they thought they wanted something and then changed their minds once they had it.

4

52a

A dog had a pot. The dog put two rocks in the pot. He put a box in the pot. He put a log in the pot. The pot was very hot.

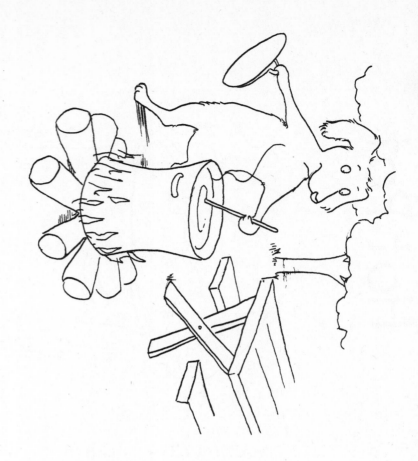

Two hogs saw the pot. "We want the pot!" they said. The dog would not give them the pot. "What can we do?" said the hogs.

Story Comprehension

What happened in "The Bug Bath"?
Read the sentences below.
Write **T** next to the things that happened.
Write **F** next to the things that didn't happen.

1. _____ Al and Bob wish to have a bath.

2. _____ Al hops into the small van.

3. _____ A duck falls into the tub.

4. _____ Bob and Al give the duck a hat.

5. _____ A fish falls into the tub.

6. _____ The boy picks up the fish.

7. _____ Bob and Al run.

8. _____ Bob and Al take a bath in a flower.

8 Book 1.2
The Bug Bath

At Home: Have children draw a picture that describes one
of the sentences they marked **T**.

53

A Map

This is a hippity-hop **map**.
It shows where the frog goes.

Look at the map.
Write the correct answer on the line.

1. Start at the lily pad. How
   many hops to the boat? _____

2. How many hops from
   the boat to the dock? _____

3. How many hops from
   the dock to the rock? _____

4. How many hops from
   the boat to the rock? _____

At Home: Have children draw a hippity-hop map of a room
in their house.

Book 1.2
The Bug Bath   4

McGraw-Hill School Division

Short *o*

dot	log	dog	jog	rod	fog

Use the words in the box to answer the riddles.

1. I wag my tail. What am I?

2. I come from a tree. What am I?

3. You catch fish with me. What am I?

4. You do this when you run. What is it?

5. You can not see if I am here. What am I?

6. I am a small spot. What am I?

At Home: Make up a simple sentence using a short **o** word. Say the sentence, omitting the word, and ask children to guess the word. Then reverse roles.

Short *o, u, i, a; ck*

Look at the pictures.
Use the words in the box to complete the rhymes.

sack	dig	fox	rug	bat

_____
- - - - - - - -

1. The _____ has my socks.

_____
- - - - - - - -

2. The pig likes to _____.

_____
- - - - - - - -

3. The _____ goes with a cap.

_____
- - - - - - - -

4. The bug is on the _____.

_____
- - - - - - - -

5. Pack your _____.

At Home: Challenge children to make up a new rhyme for one of the words in the box.

McGraw-Hill School Division

Story Elements

The **characters** are the people or animals a story is about.

The **plot** is what happens.

Read the story, then circle the answer to each question.

Max and Bob go out. It is very wet.
Max hears a sob. What is it? Max and Bob look.
Then they see a pup. The pup sits in the mud.
Bob and Max take him home. They give him ham.
Bob and Max call the pup "Lucky."

1. Who are the characters?

Max, the pup

Bob, Max

Max, Bob, the pup

2. What do Max and Bob find?

a cat

a pup

a hog

3. What do Max and Bob do?

take the pup home

pat the pup

jog with the pup

4. What do they give the pup?

ham

nuts

fish

At Home: Ask children to think of three more things that Max, Bob and Lucky can do together. Then have them draw pictures showing one of these things.

Inflectional Ending *-ed*

Add **-ed** to a word to tell about something that happened in the past.

Add **-ed** to each word.

1. rock + ed = _____

2. dash + ed = _____

3. lock + ed = _____

4. pick + ed = _____

Write the new word that completes each sentence.

5. Pat _____ the hut.

6. Jen _____ her pup to sleep.

7. Sam _____ at the dish.

8. Bob _____ home.

At Home: Invite children to draw a picture to go with each word.

Book 1.2
The Bug Bath   8

McGraw-Hill School Division

Short e

Circle the word that names the picture.
Then write the word on the line.

1.  hen

   deck

   _____

2.  leg

   beg

   _____

3. bed

   met

   _____

4.  net

   shed

   _____

5.  vet

   neck

   _____

6.  gem

   pen

   _____

6 Book 1.2
Splash!

At Home: Have children make flash cards of words that
have the short **e** sound.

High-Frequency Words

good	into	put	away

Write the word from the box that completes each
sentence.

_____

- - - - - - - - - -

1. That dish was _____!

_____

- - - - - - - - - -

2. Sam went far_____.

_____

- - - - - - - - - -

3. The dog ran _____ the shed.

_____

- - - - - - - - - -

4. She _____ the hat in a box.

At Home: Ask children to make up sentences using each of
these four words.

Book 1.2
Splash!   4

McGraw-Hill School Division

Ben the Gem

Ben's red rag is wet. What is this? There is a gem in the hem. It is good the man did not get the gem. It is good I have my pet. Ben is my gem.

4

At Home: Invite children to talk about what they would do if they lost a pet or something else of value to them.

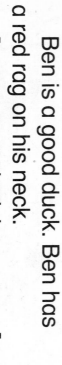

Ben is a good duck. Ben has a red rag on his neck.

I put my pet duck into a pen. I get into bed.

But a man with a net is in the pen! He gets my pet.

I want my pet. I will find him. I see Ben and the man. They are on the deck of a ship. The man lets Ben go. My pet is back.

Story Comprehension

Read these sentences.
Circle the sentences that describe what happened
in "Splash!"

1. Meg puts on her hat.

2. The hen gets the boots.

3. The cat gets a box.

4. The pets sit in the shed.

5. Meg puts on her coat.

6. Meg sees her wet pets.

7. Meg runs away.

8. The bus comes.

8 Book 1.2
Splash!

At Home: Have children draw a picture that illustrates one
of the sentences they circled.

61

A Map

This is Pam's footprint **map**.
It shows where Pam goes.

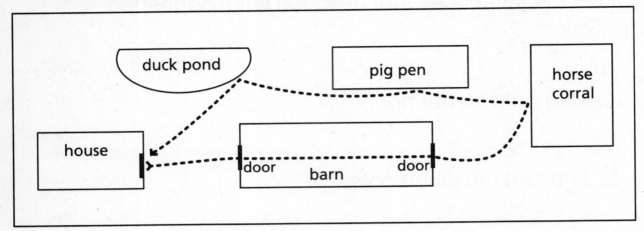

Look at the map.
Write the word to complete each sentence.

_____

\- - - - - - - - - - -

1. Pam went in and out of the _____ .

_____

\- - - - - - - - - - -

2. Pam left the barn and saw the _____ .

_____

\- - - - - - - - - - -

3. Pam saw the _____ next.

4. Pam passed the duck pond and went into the

_____

\- - - - - - - - - - -

_____ .

At Home: Have children draw a footprint map for an area around their home.

Book 1.2
Splash!   4

McGraw-Hill School Division

Short *e*

Write the word from the box that names each picture.

peck	fed	ten	vet	bed	jet

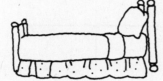

1. _____

2. _____

3. _____

4. _____

5. _____

6. _____

McGraw-Hill School Division

 6 Book 1.2
Splash!

At Home: Help children think of words that rhyme with
the words above.

63

Short *e, o, u, i, a; th*

Circle the word that names each picture.
Then print the word on the line.

1.  bat
mat

_____

- - - - - - - - - - -

_____

2.  lip
rip

_____

- - - - - - - - - - -

_____

3.  thin
thick

_____

- - - - - - - - - - -

_____

4.  sun
bun

_____

- - - - - - - - - - -

_____

5.  shock
rock

_____

- - - - - - - - - - -

_____

6.  men
neck

_____

- - - - - - - - - - -

_____

At Home: Have children think of other words that rhyme
with the words on this page.

Book 1.2
Splash 6

McGraw-Hill School Division

Main Idea

Circle the sentence that tells about the picture.

1.

The pigs live here.

The cats live here.

2.

I see the cat.

I see the rain.

3.

The dog likes the rain.

The cat likes the rain.

4.

Ducks play here.

Cows play here.

5.

Cats play here.

Mice play here.

McGraw-Hill School Division

5 Book 1.2
Splash!

At Home: Ask children to find a picture in a book or magazine. Have them explain the main idea of the picture.

65

Context Clues

Pictures or other words in a sentence can help you figure out words you don't know.

Circle the answer.

1. Ted and his cat sat on a <u>cot</u>.
Ted liked this bed.

A cot is: a bed   a box

2. The hen will <u>peck</u> the dog.
The dog will not like it.

A peck is: a nip or tap   a lick

3. See the cat <u>dash</u>.
He ran into the hut.

Dash means: to run   to pet

4. The dog has a <u>bath</u>.
She washes the mud away.

A bath is: sad   wet

At Home: Ask children to draw a picture for each underlined word on this page.

Book 1.2
Splash!   4

McGraw-Hill School Division

Blends

Read the words in the box. Then write the word that names each picture.

hill	gruff	slug	frog	flap

1. _____

2. _____

3. _____

4. _____

5. _____

6 Book 1. 2
What Bug Is It?

At Home: Have children use two of the words in a sentence.

67

High-Frequency Words

Write the words from the box to complete the letter.

about	again	around	use

Dear Grandma,

    Today we saw a movie. It was

_____

_____ bugs. How do bugs get

_____

_____? They _____

wings! I want to see the bug movie

_____

_____.

From,
Meg

At Home: Help children to write a letter to a friend or relative.

Book 1. 2
What Bug Is It? 4

McGraw-Hill School Division

Jill and Her Doll

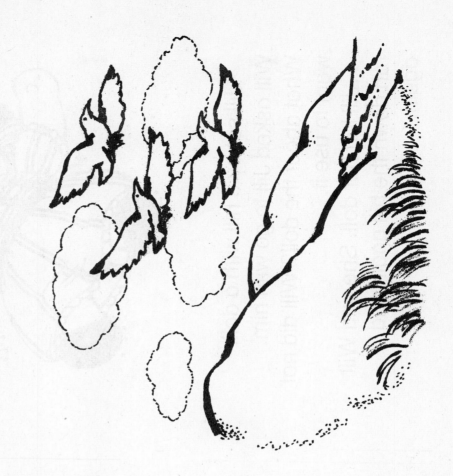

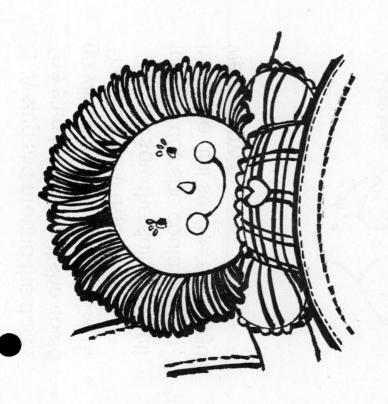

Soon Will went home.
Then Jill saw her doll. She
put the doll in her pack. Then Jill
and the doll ran up and down the
hill again and again.

4

At Home: Invite children to talk about their favorite
toys and what games they like to play with them.

Jill sat by a hill with a doll.
Will asked Jill to go with him.
What about the doll? Will did not
want to use it.

Jill left her doll. She and Will
ran down the hill again and
again.

A slug slid around the doll.
The slug told the doll she could
go with him. The doll sat there.
The slug went away.

A gull saw the doll. The gull
told the doll she could go with
him. The doll sat there. The gull
went away.

Story Comprehension

Think about "What Bug Is It?" Then read the sentences. Use the names of bugs to complete the sentences.

butterfly   ants   ladybug   bee   spider

BEGINNING

1. Rick can see bugs in a hill. He sees _____.

MIDDLE

2. Jill sees a red and black _____.

3. Nell looks at a _____ in a web.

4. Yan sees a _____ flap and flap.

END

5. The last bug they see is a _____.

5   Book 1.2
What Bug Is It?

At Home: Ask children to draw a picture of one of the bugs from the story.

69

McGraw-Hill School Division

A Map

A **street map** shows you where places are.

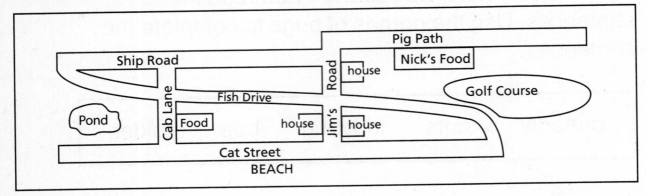

Look at the map.

1. What street is next to the beach?

_____

- -

_____

2. On what two streets can you buy food?

_____

- -

_____

3. What road has three houses?

_____

- -

_____

4. What street is next to the golf course?

_____

- -

_____

At Home: Have children draw a simple street map of your neighborhood.

Book 1.2
What Bug Is It? 4

Blends

Look at each picture.
Then write the word from the box that describes the picture.

sniff	flag	pass	smash	slam	doll

1. _____

2. _____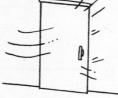

3. _____

4. _____

5. _____

6. _____

6 Book 1.2
What Bug Is It?

At Home: Choose a page from a familiar story. Help children to see how many words that begin with the letters **fr-**, **sn-**, and **sl-** they can find on that page.

71

Blends; *sh, th, ck*

Write the word from the box that names each picture.

kiss	frog	puff	smash	thrill

1. 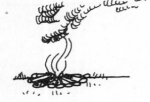 _____

2.  _____

3.  _____

4.  _____

5. _____

At Home: Have children write a short story using four of the words above.

Book 1.2
What Bug Is It? 6

McGraw-Hill School Division

Main Idea

Read the story.

Dad made a big fire.

Ann helped put up the tent.

Jim cooked hot dogs.

They had fun camping.

Does the sentence tell the main idea of the story?
Write **yes** or **no**.

1. Dad made a big fire. _____

2. They had fun camping. _____

3. Jim cooked hot dogs. _____

4. Ann helped put up the tent. _____

5. Write the sentence that tells the main idea.

_____

_____

5 Book 1.2
What Bug Is It?

At Home: Show a picture from a magazine or book, and
have children tell the main idea of the picture.

73

Context Clues

When you don't know what a word means, the words around it can help you find the meaning.

Write the word from the story that helps you know the meaning of the underlined word.

1. Jill saw a <u>slim</u> man. This thin man was her dad.

_____

- - - - - - - - -

_____

2. Meg saw Tim <u>dash</u> up the path. Then he ran past her.

_____

- - - - - - - - -

_____

3. My pup was <u>ill</u>. "I wish you were not sick." I said.

_____

- - - - - - - - -

_____

4. I shut the lid. "Do not <u>slam</u> it," said Nash.

_____

- - - - - - - - -

_____

At Home: With children, use one of the sentences on this page as a story starter.

Book 1.2
What Bug Is It? 4

McGraw-Hill School Division

Blends, Short Vowels

Circle the word to complete each sentence.
Then write it.

1. _____ tub

I get into the _____. pup

2. _____ frock

The _____ likes to jump. frog

3. _____ vet

The cat is at the _____. wet

4. _____ flap

She can _____ her wings. flat

5. _____ snack

I ate a _____ . snag

6. _____ smash

What is that good _____? smell

6 Book 1.2
A Vet

At Home: Ask children to illustrate one of these sentences.
Have them write the sentence below their drawing.

75

High-Frequency Words

Circle the word to finish each sentence.

small	out	good	want

out

1. I will go _____ to play.   small

good

2. This is a _____ book.   out

good

3. My sisters _____ a pup.   want

want

4. Some pets are _____.   small

At Home: Ask children to create their own sentences using the words **small**, **out**, **good**, and **want**.

Book 1.2
A Vet   4

McGraw-Hill School Division

My Dog Mack

"Bark! Bark!"
That is Mack. He can swim.
He can get my hat for me. He
swims to the rock. He comes
back with my hat.
"Thank you, Mack!" I say.
"Now let us go back home!"

At Home: Have children draw a picture of a windy day. Encourage them to show what can happen when it is windy.

My small dog Mack wants to go out. That is good. I want to go out, too. It is windy. I take my hat.

Mack has his ball. I toss the ball. Mack runs fast and gets the ball. Mack runs fast and gets the ball.

A small gust of wind gets my hat. It is up in the sky. I run. I cannot get my hat! Now my hat is on a rock. The rock is in a creek. I still cannot get my hat!

Story Comprehension

Write **X** next to each sentence that describes "A Vet."

I. _____ Vets help hogs.

2. _____ Vets help people get well.

3. _____ Vets see sick cats.

4. _____ A vet can help a sick duck.

5. _____ A vet will not go to a farm.

6. _____ We take pets to the vet.

6 Book 1.2
   A Vet

At Home: Help children to use these sentences to write a summary of "A Vet."

77

A Map

This is a **map** of a neighborhood.

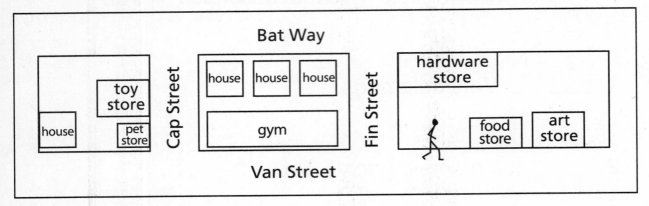

Look at the map. Write the answer to each question on the line.

1. What street has three houses on it?

_____

- - - - - - - - - - - - - - - - - - - -

_____

2. What kinds of stores are on Cap Street?

_____

- - - - - - - - - - - - - - - - - - - -

_____

                              _____

                              - - - - - - - - - - - - - -

3. What is next to the food store? _____

4. On what two streets is the hardware store?

_____

- - - - - - - - - - - - - - - - - - - -

_____

At Home: Have children draw a path or street in your neighborhood that includes one or two landmarks.

Book 1.2
A Vet   4

McGraw-Hill School Division

Story Elements

Character - (tells who)	Plot - (tells what happens)
Bill the bug	makes a wish
Pam the pig	finds cash in the mud
Liz the duck	sees the vet

Use the lists to write your own story. Write at least four sentences.

_____

- -

_____

- -

_____

- -

_____

- -

_____

- -

_____

Main Idea

Read each story.
Fill in the circle by the title that tells the main idea of the story.

1. The bird can talk.

It sings.

It is pretty.

○ This Bird Is Fun

○ Big Birds

2. The ship is big.

It goes far.

It is fast.

○ Blue Ships

○ Ships Are Great

3. Tigers are big.

They hunt.

People like tigers.

○ All About Tigers

○ A Day at the Zoo

4. The truck is red.

It has many hoses.

They shoot water.

○ The Hat

○ The Firetruck

At Home: Have children give the main idea for a story they
have read.

Book 1.2
A Vet

4

Inflectional Ending -ed

Draw a line to the word that completes the sentence.

1. The hen _____ at the mud.   pecked

2. Ned _____ in the pond.   jumped

3. Jan _____ the cat.   fished

4. Nell _____ out of bed.   kissed

4 Book 1.2
A Vet

At Home: Ask children to use one of these sentences as
the first line in a poem.

81

Context Clues

Use the pictures and sentences to help you figure out what the underlined word means. Circle the answer.

1. Jack has a <u>shed</u> down the path.

A shed is like a   shack   bed

2. The hat has a <u>rip</u>.
It is torn.

A rip is a   cap   hole

3. The cat <u>sniffs</u> the dish.

The cat   smells the dish   kicks the dish

4. The <u>thin</u> dog wants a snack.

To be thin is to be   thick   slim

At Home: Write a new sentence with children to show the meaning of one of the answer words.

Book 1.2
A Vet   4

McGraw-Hill School Division

High-Frequency Words Review

Write a word from the box to complete each sentence.

want	away	put	use	about	very

1. I _____ to go to bed.

2. She wants to _____ the big cup.

3. Could you _____ the cat out?

4. The frog is _____ wet.

5. Can you put your toys _____ ?

6. What is the book _____ ?

McGraw-Hill School Division

6 Book 1.2
High-Frequency Words Review

At Home: Have children draw a picture for two of the sentences.

83

High-Frequency Words Review

Write the word from the box that completes each sentence.

two	ride	saw	around

1. Meg will _____ fast.

2. I see _____ ducks.

3. They go _____ the shed.

4. Bob _____ the bug.

At Home: Have children use each word they wrote in another sentence.

Book 1.2
High-Frequency Words Review

4

McGraw-Hill School Division

Blends

Sound out and say each word. Print the word on the line. Then circle the picture it names.

1. spin

_____

- - - - - - - - - - - -

2. mend

_____

- - - - - - - - - - - -

3. dump

_____

- - - - - - - - - - - -

4. gust

_____

- - - - - - - - - - - -

5. king

_____

- - - - - - - - - - - -

6. lift

_____

- - - - - - - - - - - -

6 Book 1.3
Stan's Stunt

At Home: Have children use the words they wrote in a sentence.

85

High-Frequency Words

try	fall	their	would

Look at the picture. Choose a word from the box to finish each sentence.

_____
- - - - - - - -
1. I'll _____ on a hat.

_____
- - - - - - - -
2. Do not _____ into the bath.

_____
- - - - - - - -
3. See _____ new dog.

_____
- - - - - - - -
4. I _____ like to swim.

At Home: Invite children to write and illustrate one more sentence using a high-frequency word.

Book 1.3
Stan's Stunt   4

McGraw-Hill School Division

The Raft

The man held a belt for Jack to grab. Jack got it.

The man got Jack and Pam back to their camp. Pam and Jack had a rest. It was good to be off the raft!

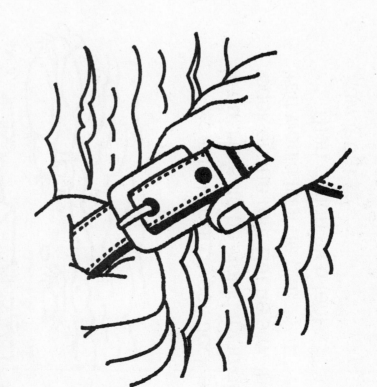

At Home: Have children tell about a trip they took. Was it fun? What was special about it?

4

86a

Pam and Jack had a raft.
They got on. Their raft went fast.
Pam and Jack did not see the
log. The raft hit the log. It made
Jack jump. Pam saw him fall into
the water.

Stan's Stunt McGraw-Hill School Division

Pam held out a vest. Jack put
it on. He said he would try to get
back on the raft. But he saw the
raft would tilt if he did.
   Then a man by a tent
saw them.

Story Comprehension

Think about "Stan's Stunt." Then circle the answer to complete each sentence.

1. Stan is a   pig   skunk   dog

2. Owl's stunt is to   blink   rest   jog

3. Frog's stunt is to   rest   swim   jump

4. Bat went   blink wink   flip flop   jump bump

5. Stan can wiggle his   tail   leg   back

McGraw-Hill School Division

5   Book 1.3
Stan's Stunt

At Home: Have children draw a picture for one of the sentences.

87

A Diagram

This is a **diagram** of a frog. It shows the parts of a frog's body.

eyes

mouth

legs

feet

Write the correct answer on the line.

1. What is the biggest part of the frog's head? _____

2. How many toes are on the frog's rear foot? _____

3. Where on the frog's body are its eyes? _____

4. How many legs does a frog have? _____

At Home: Have children draw a diagram of a favorite animal and mark some of its parts such as eyes, ears, nose, body, legs, and tail.

88

Book 1.3
Stan's Stunt 4

McGraw-Hill School Division

Blends

Read these sounds aloud. Choose the sound that completes each word. Then write the letters on the line.

sk	sp	st	nd	ng	nt	mp	ft

1. si _____

2. ju _____

3. te _____

4. so _____

5. ne _____

6. _____ ip

7. _____ ill

8. se _____

At Home: Ask children to think of three more words that contain letter combinations from the box.

Blends

Use the words in the box to complete the questions below.

send	sniff	frog	slot	fill	sing

_____

- - - - - - - - -

1. Did you _____ the cup?

_____

- - - - - - - - -

2. Birds can _____.

_____

- - - - - - - - -

3. I _____ the gift.

_____

- - - - - - - - -

4. The _____ hops around.

_____

- - - - - - - - -

5. Put a coin in the _____.

_____

- - - - - - - - -

6. I _____ the flower.

At Home: Have children turn the sentences above into questions.

Book 1.3
Stan's Stunt 6

Story Elements

The **setting** is where and when a story takes place.

Put an **X** next to each word on the list that could describe a setting.

1. _____ farm

2. _____ dog

3. _____ hut

4. _____ class

5. _____ camp

6. _____ shirt

7. _____ path

8. _____ bus

9. _____ hill

10. _____ shed

11. _____ wig

12. _____ jet

McGraw-Hill School Division

12 Book 1.3
Stan's Stunt

At Home: Ask children to think of a good setting for a
story. Then have them tell a story based on that setting.

91

Possessives

Apostrophe (') s at the end of a name or thing means that the person or thing owns something.

Write the words to show who owns something. Remember to add **'s**.

1. Jack   cat   _____

2. bird   nest   _____

3. Kim   ship   _____

4. king   gems   _____

5. Tom   lamp   _____

6. dog   stick   _____

At Home: Invite children to illustrate a few of the examples above.

Book 1.3
Stan's Stunt   6

McGraw-Hill School Division

Blends

Read each of the blends. Write one blend to complete the name of each picture.

tw	pl	pr	cr	tr

1. _____ ab

2. _____ op

3. _____ ess

4. _____ ash

5. _____ ist

5   Book 1.3
Greg's Mask

At Home: Help children find other words in books and magazines that begin with the consonant blends above.

93

High-Frequency Words

Read each sentence. Circle the word that completes the sentence. Then write the word.

new	old	any	grow

1. I need _____ pants. new any

2. Do you have _____ red pants? any grow

3. My _____ pants have a rip. any old

4. I want to _____ very tall. new grow

At Home: Ask children to write sentences using each of the high-frequency words.

Book 1.3
Greg's Mask 4

McGraw-Hill School Division

The Trash Plant

Bob put a new bat in the plant.
"No," said the man. "New things are still good. We can use them again."
"Good idea!" said Bob.

At Home: Have children name other things that might end up in a trash plant.

4

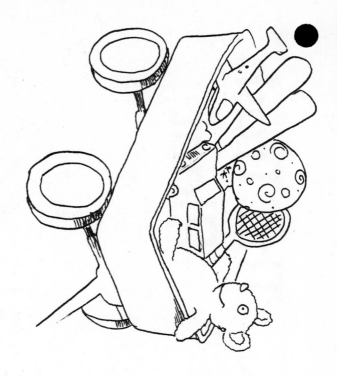

"Any old bats?" said the man.

"I have a new one," said the man.

"No new bats," said the man.

"I want old bats for my trash plant."

"What is a trash plant?" Bob said.

"Come with me," said the man.

The trash plant was a big blob. Plop! The man put a clock in the plant. Clang! Clack! Bump! "I grow plump when you dump," said the trash plant.

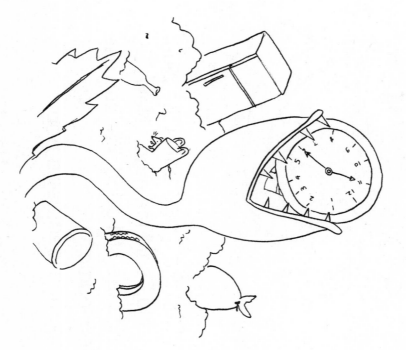

Story Comprehension

Read each sentence about "Greg's Mask."
Write the name of the person it describes.

Miss Willis	Greg	Tam

1. Her class did a skit.

2. He made a mask.

3. She did not like the mask.

4. He put the mask in the trash.

5. She said, "Where is your mask?"

6. She came to school with the mask.

6 Book 1.3
Greg's Mask

At Home: Have children draw pictures of animal faces
that would make good masks.

95

A Diagram

This is a **diagram** of a sports center. The diagram shows what can be played at the center.

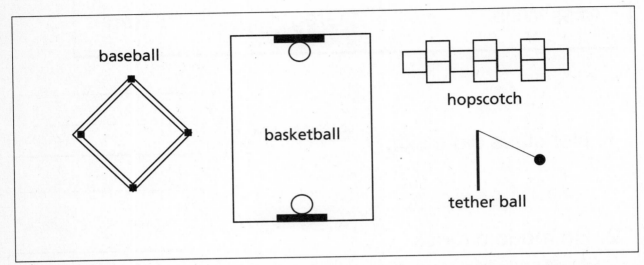

baseball

basketball

hopscotch

tether ball

Draw a line from each question on the left to the correct answer on the right.

1. Where would you hit a ball?

A. basketball court

2. Where would you throw a ball into a basket?

B. baseball diamond and tether ball area

3. Where would you bounce a ball?

C. hopscotch area

4. Where would you hop?

D. basketball court

At Home: Have children make a drawing of one or two pieces of equipment used in sports or games.

Book 1.3
Greg's Mask

4

McGraw-Hill School Division

Blends

Say each word. Print the word on the line.
Then circle the picture it names.

1. c r i b

_____

- - - - - - - - - - -

_____

2. p r i n t

_____

- - - - - - - - - - -

_____

3. p l a n t

_____

- - - - - - - - - - -

_____

4. t r i c k

_____

- - - - - - - - - - -

_____

5. t w i g

_____

- - - - - - - - - - -

_____

6. c r a c k

_____

- - - - - - - - - - -

_____

Blends

Look at the picture. Read the question. Then write the answer.

1. Is this a **crab** or a **crack**?

_____

_ _ _ _ _ _ _ _ _ _ _ _ _ _

_____

2. Do old cans go in the **twist** or in the **trash**?

_____

_ _ _ _ _ _ _ _ _ _ _ _ _ _

_____

3. Does the boy **print** his name or **plan** it?

_____

_ _ _ _ _ _ _ _ _ _ _ _ _ _

_____

John

4. Is this a **plug** or a **plant**?

_____

_ _ _ _ _ _ _ _ _ _ _ _ _ _

_____

5. Is the bird on a **twig** or a **truck**?

_____

_ _ _ _ _ _ _ _ _ _ _ _ _ _

_____

At Home: Have children look through books to find three words that begin with **pl**.

Book 1.3
Greg's Mask   5

McGraw-Hill School Division

Compare and Contrast

Read the story and look at the pictures.
Then answer the questions.

Scott and Sara are twins.
They were born on the same day.
They have the same mother and father.
They live in the same house.
Scott likes to play ball. Sara likes to swim.

I. Tell how Scott and Sara are alike.

_____

- - - - - - - - - - - - - - - - - - -

_____

- - - - - - - - - - - - - - - - - - -

_____

2. Tell how Scott and Sara are different.

_____

- - - - - - - - - - - - - - - - - - -

_____

- - - - - - - - - - - - - - - - - - -

_____

McGraw-Hill School Division

6 Book 1.3
Greg's Mask

At Home: Have children suggest other ways in which
Scott and Sara could be alike and different.

99

Possessives

Read each sentence. Circle the word that completes the sentence. Then write the word.

1. This is _____ drum.

   Glen   Glen's

2. I see _____.

   Pam   Pam's

3. Two _____ pecked my leg.

   hens   hen's

4. _____ duck quacks.

   Rick   Rick's

McGraw-Hill School Division

ch, wh, nk

Read the words. Then read the riddles. Choose a word to answer each riddle.

chick	when	branch	wink

1.

I am a small bird.

What am I?

_____

- - - - - - - - -

_____

2.

I am one eye, closed and opened.

What am I?

_____

- - - - - - - - -

_____

3.

I am the arm of a tree.

What am I?

_____

- - - - - - - - -

_____

4.

Ask me what time it happened.

What are you asking?

_____

- - - - - - - - -

_____

4 Book 1.3
Sam's Songs

At Home: Ask children to circle the consonant blends in each word and recite the word.

101

High-Frequency Words

Read the story.

Bob and Jen

Bob and Jen have lunch together.

They sit on the bench.

They eat their snacks.

They drink some milk, too.

Now they are singing a song.

Now retell the story. Write the words on the lines where they belong.

now	eat	too	together

_____

- - - - - - - - - - - -

1. Bob and Jen sit _____.

_____

- - - - - - - - - - - -

2. They _____ their lunch.

_____

- - - - - - - - - - - -

3. They have a drink, _____.

_____

- - - - - - - - - - - -

4. _____ they are singing a song.

At Home: Ask children to use the words they wrote in a story about something they did with a friend.

Book1.3
Sam's Song   4

McGraw-Hill School Division

The Chomp Champs

The two men went to eat. Who will be the champ? Chet ate a ranch. Chomp! Hank ate a bank. Chomp!

Chet could eat no more. Hank could eat no more. Now they are champs together.

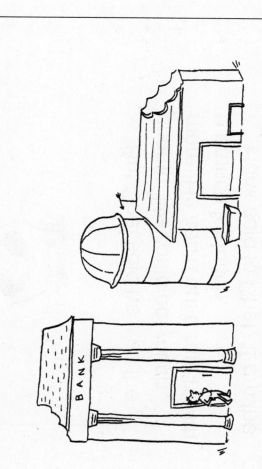

4

Hank was very big. Hank
would eat a lot. For lunch, he
would eat a bunk bed. He would
munch and munch.
"I am the champ," said Hank.

Sam's Song McGraw-Hill School Division

But Chet said he was the
champ. He could eat much
more. He could eat a ranch with
a branch for lunch.
Hank said to Chet, "I am the
champ. I can eat a bank and a
sink, too."

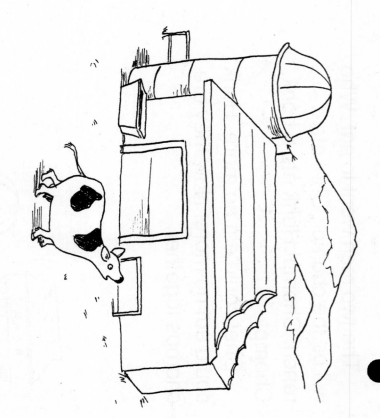

Story Comprehension

Think about the story, "Sam's Song." Circle **true** if a statement is true. Circle **false** if it is not true.

I. Chuck is Sam's father.   true   false

2. Chuck is Sam's brother.   true   false

3. Chuck and Sam are owls.   true   false

4. Sam is a baby owl.   true   false

5. Sam has a big song.   true   false

6. Mom, Dad, Chuck, and Sam like to sing.   true   false

7. A small song is not a good song.   true   false

8. Sam likes her own song.   true   false

8 Book1.3
Sam's Song

At Home: Invite children to illustrate one of the true statements.

103

A Diagram

This **diagram** shows different sizes of dogs.

Husky   Great Dane   Beagle   Labrador

Look at the diagram. Write the answer to each
question on the line.

1. Which dog is the smallest? _____

2. Which dog is the largest? _____

3. Which dog is larger
than a Beagle and
smaller than a Labrador? _____

4. Which is the second-largest dog? _____

At Home: Ask children to draw their two favorite animals
and identify which one is larger.

Book 1.3
Sam's Songs   4

ch, wh, nk

Print the word on the line. Then circle the picture it names.

1. check _____

3. bench _____

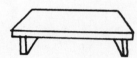 

4. bank _____

5. chin _____

6. drink _____

5 | Book 1.3
Sam's Songs

At Home: Have children choose one of the blends reviewed on this page and make up a verse using the blend, such as "Chad chewed chunks of chocolate-chip cookies."

ch, wh, nk; **Blends**

Circle the word that completes the sentence.
Then write the word on the line.

1. The ship

_____

- - - - - - - - - -

_____.

sank   drank

2. I crunch on a

_____

- - - - - - - - - -

_____.

chill   chip

3. The cash is in the

_____

- - - - - - - - - -

_____.

yank   bank

4. She ate her

_____

- - - - - - - - - -

_____.

lunch   branch

5. Do you play

_____

- - - - - - - - - -

_____?

chess   chin

6. I go home

_____

- - - - - - - - - -

_____ Dan does.

when   whisk

McGraw-Hill School Division

Compare and Contrast

Use the chart to show how a scissors and a knife are alike and different. Put an **x** in the box next to the words that tell about each one.

	scissors	knife
one blade		
cuts food		
two blades		
sharp		
made of steel		
cuts paper		

At Home: Have children name other things that can be cut with a pair of scissors or a knife.

Contractions

A **contraction** is a short form of two words.
An **apostrophe (')** takes the place of the letters
that are left out.

Draw a line from the words on the left to the correct
contraction on the right. Then write each
contraction on the line.

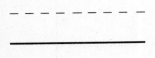

1. can not   can't

2. we will   don't

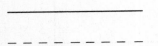

3. do not   she's

4. is not   I've

5. I have   isn't

6. she is   we'll

Book 1.3
Sam's Song   6

McGraw-Hill School Division

Long *a: a-e*

Read the words to yourself. Circle the correct word.
Then write it to complete each sentence.

1. Jake lives by a _____.

lake
late

2. James has a pet _____.

grape
snake

3. Jake can _____.

wade
make

4. Jake can _____.

case
skate

5. Jake will go to his _____.

cave
cake

5 Book 1.3
Snakes

At Home: Have children use the words they did not circle
in sentences.

109

High-Frequency Words

Circle the word that completes each sentence.
Then write the word.

_____
- - - - - - - -
1. _____ is the dog?   Where   Know

_____
- - - - - - - -
2. I _____ where he is.   why   know

_____
- - - - - - - -
3. The dog is _____ there.   where   under

_____
- - - - - - - -
4. _____ is he hiding?   Why   Under

At Home: Have children draw a picture illustrating one of the
sentences.

Book 1.3
Snakes   4

McGraw-Hill School Division

The Snake Cake

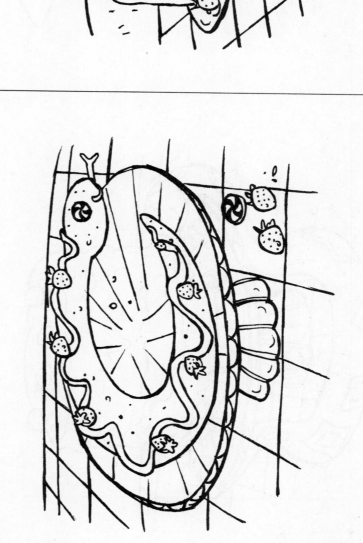

Jake is brave. Jane is happy. She makes Jake a big cake. It is in the shape of a snake. Why? It is her way to say thank you to Jake!

At Home: Invite children to draw a picture of a cake shaped like an animal.

4

110a

Jake saw a cake. He liked cake. But the cake was for the bake sale. It was not for him.

"Will Jane make me a cake?" asked Jake. He did not know.

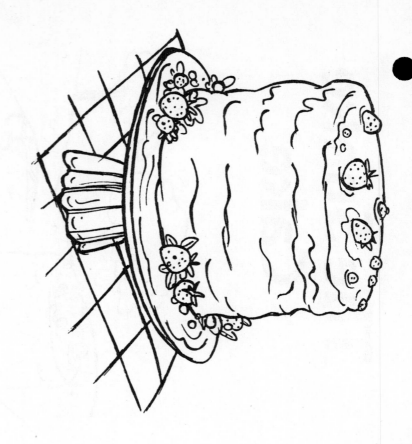

What was that? It was a snake. Jane did not like snakes. Where was it? It was under the cake plate. Jake got it.

"I will take the snake out," Jake said to Jane.

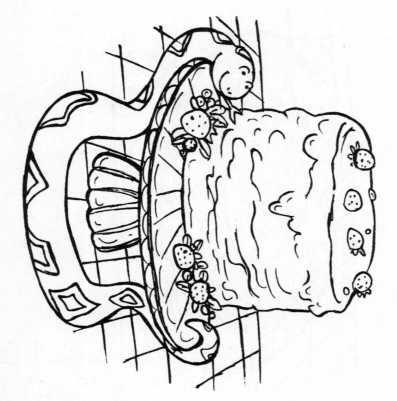

Story Comprehension

Think about what you have learned in "Snakes."
Draw a line to the word that completes each
sentence.

1. Snakes live in   rat

2. A snake can chomp a   pets

3. Snakes have no   slip

4. A snake can hang from a   legs

5. A snake can twist and   branch

6. Some snakes make good   lakes

At Home: Have children name other animals that can live
in trees.

McGraw-Hill School Division

A Diagram

The **diagram** shows different kinds of snakes.

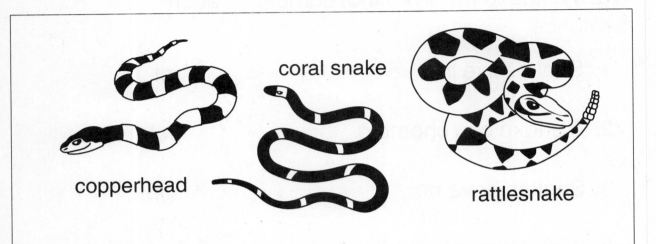

coral snake

copperhead

rattlesnake

Complete each sentence.

1. The _____ is the thickest snake.

2. The _____ is the thinnest snake.

3. The _____ is wider than the coral snake and thinner than the rattlesnake.

4. The _____ and the coral snake both have stripes.

At Home: Have children draw two snakes of different widths.

112

Book 1.3
Snakes

4

McGraw-Hill School Division

Long *a: a-e*

Choose the word to complete each sentence.
Write the word on the line.

make	safe	game	grade

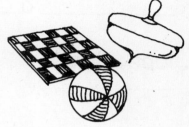

1. Shall we play a fun _____?

2. I want to _____ a cake.

3. I cross when it is _____.

4. We are in first _____.

4 Book 1.3
Snakes

At Home: Have children identify things in the house
whose names begin with the short **a** sound.

113

a-e; ch, wh, nk

Write the words to make each sentence tell about
the picture.

1. bake   chase   cake   rank

_____   _____

_ _ _ _ _ _ _ _   _ _ _ _ _ _ _ _

_____ a _____

2. tape   drink   lane   punch

_____   _____

_ _ _ _ _ _ _ _   _ _ _ _ _ _ _ _

_____ some _____

3. grapes   drape   plate   flame

_____   _____

_ _ _ _ _ _ _ _   _ _ _ _ _ _ _ _

_____ on a _____

4. When   What   chip   champ

_____   _____

_ _ _ _ _ _ _ _   _ _ _ _ _ _ _ _

_____ a _____

5. chick   chill   tank   bank

_____   _____

_ _ _ _ _ _ _ _   _ _ _ _ _ _ _ _

_____ in a _____

At Home: Challenge children to think of another word
combination using two of the following words: **bank, lake,
check, chip, wade, munch.**

114

Book 1.3
Snakes   5

McGraw-Hill School Division

Compare and Contrast

Look at the pictures. Write **snake** next to the pictures that tell about snakes. Write **me** next to the pictures that tell about people.

1. _____

2. _____

3. _____

4. _____

5. _____

6. _____

7. _____

8. _____

8 Book 1.3
Snakes

At Home: Have children compare snakes to their pets or other animals such as birds or fish.

115

Contractions

A **contraction** is a short form of two words.
An **apostrophe (')** takes the place of the letters that are left out.

Write the contraction for the underlined words in each sentence.

1. <u>I will</u> go to the lake.

2. <u>We have</u> baked a cake.

3. <u>It is</u> a big tent.

4. <u>They will</u> rake grass.

5. She <u>can not</u> sit in the sun.

6. <u>I have</u> come to your house.

At Home: Invite children to write three more sentences with contractions.

McGraw-Hill School Division

a-e; ch, wh, nk; **Blends**

Use these words to answer the riddles.

chick	bank	stump	white	plane

1. You can fly in me. What am I? _____

2. I am soft and yellow. I live on a farm.

What am I? _____

3. I am the color of the clouds. _____
What am I?

4. Put your cash in me. I will save it.

What am I? _____

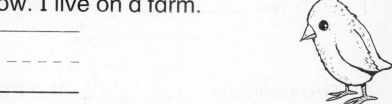

5. Cut down a tree. I am all that is left.

What am I? _____

High-Frequency Words

eat	old	try	under

Write the words from the box on the lines to complete the story.

_____

- - - - - - - -

1. Sam will _____ to catch the ball.

_____

- - - - - - - -

2. The ball falls _____ the tree.

_____

- - - - - - - -

3. Grandpa and Sam _____ lunch.

_____

- - - - - - - -

4. The tree is very _____.

At Home: Invite children to use each high-frequency word in another sentence.

Book 1.3
Let's Camp Out!

McGraw-Hill School Division

The Gum Trap

"What is that?" said Big Bud.
"It is gum," said Nate.
Big Bud chewed lots of gum.
He could not chat. He could not think.

"You will not rest! You are in a gum trap set by the best!" said Nate.

At Home: Encourage children to draw a picture of the story they read about Nate and Big Bud.

Big Bud said to Nate, "I want
to eat. Bake me a cake. I will
jump. I will bang. I will pinch you
under your chin. Make me lunch.
I will not rest until I have the best."
Nate made Big Bud a cake.

"I want to try hot dogs," Big
Bud said. "I will fling. I will
swing. I will not rest until I have
the best."
"You are an old pest," said
Nate.
Nate made Big Bud hot dogs.

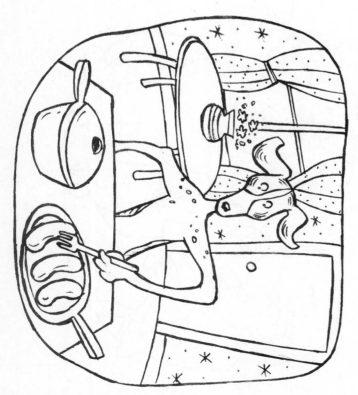

Story Comprehension

Read the statements. Underline the things you might do on a camping trip.

1. sleep in a tent

2. wade in a lake

3. shop for gifts

4. sit by a fire

5. look at the stars

6. put on a pack

7. chat on the phone

8. find a nest

9. sing songs

10. see a movie

11. see a frog

12. take a hike

12 Book 1.3
Let's Camp Out!

At Home: Have children draw a picture of something they might see on a camping trip.

119

A Diagram

This **diagram** shows how to make water safe
when you are camping.

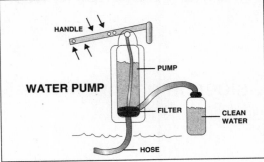

Complete the questions.

1. What makes stream water safe for drinking?

_____

- -

_____

2. What pumps the water out of the stream?

_____

- -

_____

3. What does water pass through to get to the filter?

_____

- -

_____

4. What happens last?

_____

- -

_____

At Home: Have children make a step-by-step diagram for a
simple task that they do often.

Book 1.3
Let's Camp Out! 4

McGraw-Hill School Division

Compare and Contrast

Read the sentences. If the sentence tells how things are alike, color the picture. If the sentence tells how things are different, circle the picture.

1. Jake and Pam sit in a hut.

2. Spot is small. Fluff is very big.

3. My socks are pink. My hat is pink.

4. We like to sing.

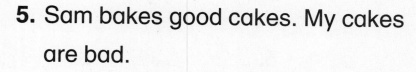

5. Sam bakes good cakes. My cakes are bad.

6. Now it is cold. Then it was hot.

McGraw-Hill School Division

6 Book 1.3
Let's Camp Out!

At Home: Ask children to compare today's weather with yesterday's weather.

121

Story Elements

The **setting** is where and when a story takes place.
Read the story.
Then circle the pictures that describe the **setting** of the park.

The Park

Brad lives in a big city.
There is a big park near him. It has lots of plants.
There are swings. Brad likes to run on the hills.
Then he sits on the bench. He likes to look at people.

1.

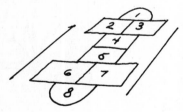

2.

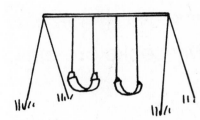

3.

4.

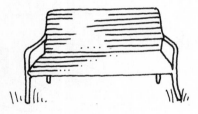

5.

6.

McGraw-Hill School Division

Possessives

An **apostrophe (')** and the letter **s** at the end of someone's name mean that person or thing owns something.

Write the words to show who owns something. Remember to add **'s**.

1. Jake tape _____

2. bird song _____

3. Kate chin _____

4. snake fangs _____

5. Jane vase _____

6. Eric brush _____

6 Book 1.3
Let's Camp Out!

At Home: Help children to add three more examples to this list.

123

Contractions

A **contraction** is a short form of two words. Some letters are replaced by an **apostrophe (')**.

Draw a line from the words to the correct contraction.

1. I will   he's

2. he is   I've

3. I have   I'll

4. they have   they've

Write the word that completes each sentence.

it's	doesn't	don't	they'll

5. Please _____ be late.

6. I think _____ come to the party.

7. I know _____ on the shelf.

8. Tom _____ like the shirt.

Book 1.3
Let's Camp Out!   8

McGraw-Hill School Division

High-Frequency Words Review

Underline the word that tells about each picture.

1.

The apple will _____.

fall   rang

2.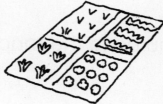

Let it _____.

grow   jump

3.

They _____ grapes.

snag   eat

4.

The _____ shack is red.

old   new

5.

He is _____ the tent.

on   under

6.

This is _____ pet pig.

bad   their

McGraw-Hill School Division

6 Book 1.3
High-Frequency Words Review

At Home: Have children make up sentences for three of
the correct answers.

High-Frequency Words Review

Circle the word that completes each sentence.

I. ___ you go to the ranch?

    Would   Skate

2. Do you have ___ trash?

    any   clock

3. I want to go ___ .

    lamp   now

4. I like the red dress ___ .

    too   sing

5. ___ did he go?

    Risk   Where

6. ___ can ducks swim?

    Why   Mud

At Home: Have children use each of the words they circled in a sentence.

126

Book 1.3
High-Frequency Words Review

6

McGraw-Hill School Division

Long *i: i-e*

Use the words in the box to answer the riddles.

fi**ve**	sm**ile**	t**ime**	b**ike**	r**ipe**

1. Six is after me. What am I? _____

2. You do this with your lips. What am I? _____

3. A good plum is this way. What am I? _____

4. A clock tells you about me. What am I? _____

5. You can ride me. What am I? _____

5 Book 1.4
The Shopping List

At Home: Have children make up sentences using each of the words in the box.

127

High-Frequency Words

Write the word from the box that completes each sentence.

after	always	blue	were	who

1. The cat runs _____ the dog.

_____
- - - - - - -

2. _____ has my hat?

_____
- - - - - - -

3. My toys _____ in the box.

_____
- - - - - - -

4. The chicks _____ eat.

_____
- - - - - - -

5. The water is _____.

Book 1.4
The Shopping List 5

McGraw-Hill School Division

The Wish Fish

Then the man wished for a kite. So the fish tied the man and his wife to the kite. Soon they were up in the sky. "Now I have my wish!" said the fish. "They are gone."

At Home: Have children draw you a picture that illustrates the story.

4

A man had a blue fish. The fish said he would give the man a wish.

The man wished that he would always have dimes.

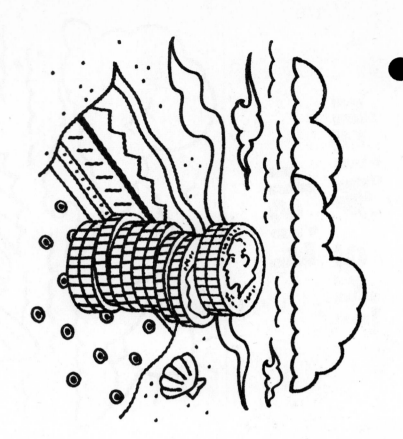

The Shopping List McGraw-Hill School Division

After that, the wife of the man made a wish. She wished for a lime and a tire. The fish, who was in the waves, gave her the wish.

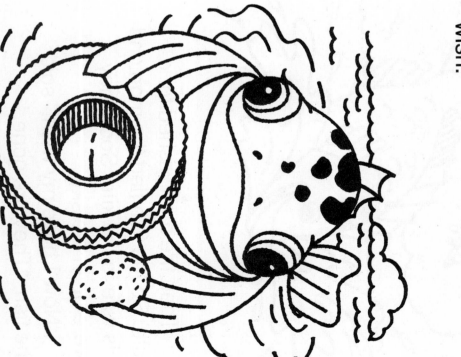

Story Comprehension

Think about what happened in "The Shopping List."
Write **T** if the sentence is **true**. Write **F** if the
sentence is **false**.

1. _____ Mike has a list.

2. _____ His dad drives a bus.

3. _____ Dad wants to know what Mike forgot.

4. _____ Dad hunts and hunts.

5. _____ Fran and Ann try to help Mike.

6. _____ At last, Miss Lin gives up.

7. _____ Mike gets sad and goes away.

8. _____ Mom wants Mike to tell Dad it is time to eat.

8 Book 1.4
The Shopping List

At Home: Help children to write a shopping list for a meal
you are planning together.

129

A Chart

Look at the **chart**.

| What You Buy in a Hardware Store ||
Kitchen	Workshop
pot	pipe
cups	lock
forks	file
cake pan	nails
plates	pump
	clamp

Write the correct answer on the line.

1. Which things are for the workshop?

_____

- -

_____

2. Which things are for the kitchen?

_____

- -

_____

3. Name something you use to eat with.

_____

- - - - - - - -

_____

4. What is something you might hit with a hammer?

_____

- - - - - - - -

_____

At Home: Have children make lists of items in the kitchen and another room at home.

Book 1.4
The Shopping List
4

McGraw-Hill School Division

Long *i: i-e*

Write the words in each group that have the same middle sound as in h**ide**.

1. bike
_____
- - - - - - - - -
_____

nine
_____
- - - - - - - - -
_____

take
_____
- - - - - - - - -
_____

2. lime
_____
- - - - - - - - -
_____

pine
_____
- - - - - - - - -
_____

cane
_____
- - - - - - - - -
_____

3. late
_____
- - - - - - - - -
_____

slide
_____
- - - - - - - - -
_____

kite
_____
- - - - - - - - -
_____

4. write
_____
- - - - - - - - -
_____

wide
_____
- - - - - - - - -
_____

wade
_____
- - - - - - - - -
_____

5. tire
_____
- - - - - - - - -
_____

ride
_____
- - - - - - - - -
_____

tale
_____
- - - - - - - - -
_____

5 Book 1.4
The Shopping List

At Home: Ask children to choose a word with the long **i** sound and use it in a sentence.

131

i-e, a-e

Circle the word that completes the sentence.
Then write it on the line.

_____
- - - - - - - -

1. They _____ the chunk.

bite   fake   wade

_____
- - - - - - - -

2. He locks the _____.

shame   gate   tale

_____
- - - - - - - -

3. Fish swim in the _____.

bake   late   lake

_____
- - - - - - - -

4. We see a bee _____.

hive   rake   size

_____
- - - - - - - -

5. The clock _____ me up.

wakes   trade   line

McGraw-Hill School Division

Cause and Effect

Look at the picture. Underline the sentence that tells what will probably happen.

1.

   He rides on a pony.

   He goes inside the house.

2.

   She fixes the tire.

   She rides to school.

3.

   She goes outside.

   She goes to bed.

4.

   The rain comes in.

   The sun comes out.

5.

   The tree has no leaves.

   The tree has many leaves.

5 Book 1.4
The Shopping List

At Home: Have children tell the cause and the effect in each situation.

133

Inflectional Endings -s, -es

Add **-s** or **-es** to tell what only one person or thing does.

When a word ends in **e** or most consonants, add **-s**.
When a word ends in **sh, ch, x,** or **ss,** add **-es.**

Circle the word that completes each sentence.
Then write the word on the line.

1. Nick _____ his pup.

   brush   brushes

2. She _____ me a ring.

   give   gives

3. They _____ for food.

   shop   hops

4. The mouse _____.

   munch munches

5. Bob and Jen _____ for fish.

   wish   wishes

6. The boy _____ the gate.

   yank   yanks

At Home: Challenge children to use three of the uncircled word choices in sentences.

Book 1.4
The Shopping List   6

McGraw-Hill School Division

Long *o: o-e*

Rose r**o**de her bike all the way h**o**me.

Name the picture. Circle the word that rhymes.
Then write the word.

1. hose   code   home   _____

2. home   rose   toad   _____

3. rode   those   home   _____

4. Rome   rode   chose   _____

5. code   home   nose   _____

6. home   hole   those   _____

McGraw-Hill School Division

6 Book 1.4
Yasmin's Ducks

At Home: Have children use rhyming pairs of words from the page to make a one-line poem.

135

High-Frequency Words

Write the words from the box to finish the sentences.

some	found	work	because	buy

_____

- - - - - - - - - - - -

1. Dad went to _____.

_____

- - - - - - - - - - - -

2. We _____ our cat.

_____

- - - - - - - - - - - -

3. I will _____ it at the store.

_____

- - - - - - - - - - - -

4. Jane is sad _____ she lost her ball.

_____

- - - - - - - - - - - -

5. Pam wants _____ chips.

At Home: Have children draw a picture to go along with one of the sentences.

Book 1.4
Yasmin's Ducks   5

McGraw-Hill School Division

Jake Gets Work

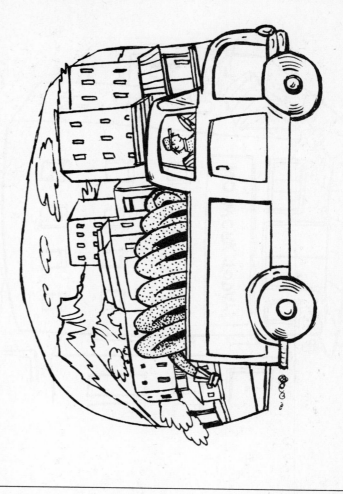

Now Jake has found a job. He puts out fires. And he is good at it. Now Jake can buy things. He has a home in Rome!

At Home: Invite children to talk about what jobs they would like to have when they are older.

4

One day Jake went to work.
But there was no work for him.
"I can go fast. I have a hose,"
Jake said. "I have to work. I
want to buy some things."

NO WORK TODAY!

Jake went in his truck
to Rome. "There must be work
here because it is big," said
Jake.
At the woods near Rome,
Jake saw smoke. He drove
close. It was a fire. He got his
hose. He put out the fire.

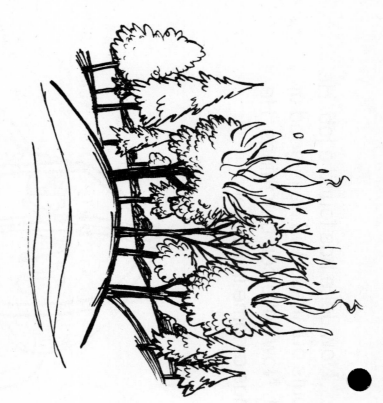

Story Comprehension

Think about "Yasmin's Ducks." Finish each
sentence by circling the picture that tells the answer.

1. Yasmin likes to draw ___.

a.    **b.**

2. Yasmin saw ducks in a ___.

a.    **b.**

3. Ducks stay dry by ___.

a.    **b.**

4. Ducks can dive in a ___.

a. 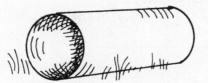   **b.**

5. The ducks can't eat when the lake is ___.

a.    **b.**

5 Book 1.4
Yasmin's Ducks

At Home: Have children tell what was their favorite part of
the story.

137

A Chart

Look at the tally **chart** below.

What Pets Do You Like Best?	
Mice llllll	Rats lllll
Cats llllllll	Birds llll
Dogs llllll	Fish lllll

This chart shows some children's favorite pets. Count the marks next to each item. Then you will know which pets the children like best.

Write the correct word to complete each sentence.

_____
- - - - - - - - -

1. The favorite pet of most of the children is a _____ .

_____
- - - - - - - -

2. _____ children like rats best.

_____
- - - - - - - - -

3. Mice and dogs each have _____ tally marks.

_____
- - - - - - - -

4. Birds have _____ tally marks.

At Home: Help children to make a tally sheet to record people's preferences about something that interests them.

McGraw-Hill School Division

Book 1.4
Yasmin's Ducks 4

Long *o: o-e*

Circle the picture in each box that has the long **o** sound as in j**oke**. Then write the word from the list that tells what the picture shows.

rose	rope	globe	cone

1.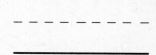

2.

3.

4.

McGraw-Hill School Division

4 Book 1.4
Yasmin's Ducks

At Home: Ask children to write a sentence using one of the words on the list.

o-e, i-e, a-e

Look at the picture. Complete each word by writing
a, **i**, or **o** in the blank.

1.

_____

- - - - - - -

sk _____ te

2.

_____

- - - - - - -

b _____ ke

3.

_____

- - - - - - -

b _____ ne

4.

_____

- - - - - - -

t _____ re

5.

_____

- - - - - - -

c _____ ne

6.

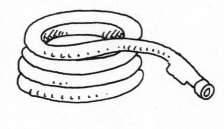

_____

- - - - - - -

h _____ se

At Home: Have children use three of the words above in sentences.

Book 1.4
Yasmin's Ducks

6

McGraw-Hill School Division

Cause and Effect

Look at each picture. It shows what happened.
Underline the sentence that tells why it happened.

Effect	**Cause**

1.

Grandma lives near us.

Grandma lives far away.

Grandma came to see us.

2.

Dad rides the bike.

Dad will go away.

Dad needs some help.

3.

They are looking for a cat.

The girl wants a new ball.

Mother wants a green hat.

4.

The dog wants the bone.

The dog will go away.

The dog hit its nose.

4 Book 1.4
Yasmin's Ducks

At Home: Challenge children to think of a sentence for
each effect picture.

141

Inflectional Ending *-ed*

Add **-ed** to show what one or more people or things did in the past.

Add **-ed** to the word. Then write the new word on the line to tell what happened in the past.

1. dash _____   Dave _____ home.

2. kiss _____   Mom _____ me.

3. jump _____   The kids _____ up.

4. pick _____   Tom _____ the plum.

5. thank _____   We _____ her.

6. drift _____   The stick _____ away.

McGraw-Hill School Division

Long *u: u-e*

Write one of the words from the box in each sentence.

flute	June	rule	mule	brute

1. I see that it is _____.

2. I can ride a _____.

3. One _____ is that we all line up.

4. The bull was a _____.

5. I will play a song on my _____.

5 Book 1.4
The Knee-High Man

At Home: Have children say each word, then write it and circle the letter **u**.

143

High-Frequency Words

Choose a word from the box to finish each sentence.

carry	been	clean	done	far

1. We will ⬚⬚⬚⬚⬚ the van.

2. We are not ⬚⬚⬚ from my home.

3. Is the cake ⬚⬚⬚⬚ yet?

4. I have ⬚⬚⬚⬚ on a ship.

5. I can ⬚⬚⬚⬚⬚ the pot on my head.

At Home: Have children draw pictures to show what the words **carry** and **clean** mean.

Book 1.4
The Knee-High Man

5

June Rules

"Can I rule June?" asked Max. "No, I cannot!" He still had far to go. But not on June. She was in her shed.

At Home: Encourage children to talk about different kinds of transportation. What is good about each kind? What may be difficult?

4

June was a mule. One day,
Max went to her clean shed.
"June will give me a ride," he
said. "I will make her carry me."
Max got his flute to play June
a tune. But June did not want a
tune!

June had been sad. Max
wanted to help her.
He got a prune for June. But
June did not want a prune.

Story Comprehension

Draw a line to connect the characters in "The Knee-High Man" to what they said.

1. June

a. Yell and eat grass to be big like me.

2. Sam the Knee-High Man

b. Sam did not grow an inch.

3. Bob Bull

c. Eat a lot of corn and run ten miles to be like me.

4. Max Mule

d. Will you tell me how I can grow?

5. Kate Owl

e. You are fine just as you are.

5 | Book 1.4
The Knee-High Man

At Home: Help children to list the order in which Sam visits the characters in the story (Max, Bob, and Kate).

145

A Chart

This **chart** tells you what Sam, Dan, and Pam said.

Sam	Dan	Pam
pack your toys	ride the train	find a home
take your dog	move in June	live in a dome

Write the answer on the line.

1. What did Pam say? _____

- -

_____

_____

- - - - - - - - - - - - - - - - -

2. Who said to take your dog? _____

_____

- -

3. What did Dan say? _____

_____

- - - - - - - - - - - - - -

4. Who said to find a home? _____

At Home: Have children make charts about what friends have said.

Book 1.4
The Knee-High Man   4

Long *u: u-e*

Look at each picture. Write the word from the box that answers each question.

dune	mule	tune	cube

1. I look like a horse. What am I?

_____

- - - - - - - - - -

_____

2. You can play me. What am I?

_____

- - - - - - - - - -

_____

3. I am made of sand. What am I?

_____

- - - - - - - - - -

_____

4. I am the shape of a box. What am I?

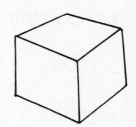

_____

- - - - - - - - - -

_____

4 Book 1.4
The Knee-High Man

At Home: Ask children to make up a riddle for one of the words from the box.

147

u-e, o-e, i-e, a-e

Read each clue. Circle the answer. Then write the word on the line.

1. Dogs eat me. What am I?

bone   bike   stone

_____

- - - - - - - - - -

I am a _____.

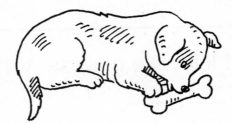

2. You stop a bike with me. What am I?

bake   broke   brake

_____

- - - - - - - - - -

I am a _____.

3. I am on a happy face. What am I?

mile   smile   slope

_____

- - - - - - - - - -

I am a _____.

4. You swim with me. What am I?

tube   poke   cube

_____

- - - - - - - - - -

I am a _____.

At Home: Have children underline all the word choices above that have the same middle sound as **stove.**

Book 1.4
The Knee-High Man   8

McGraw-Hill School Division

Make Inferences

Read each sentence. Draw a line to the person who can help.

1. I want something to eat.

2. I have a toothache.

3. I want to cross the street.

4. I broke my leg.

5. The phone is not working.

McGraw-Hill School Division

5 Book 1.4
The Knee-High Man

At Home: Have children look through magazines to find pictures of other people who are helpers.

149

Inflectional Endings *-er, -est*

Add **-er** to compare two things.
Add **-est** to compare three or more things.

Circle the word that completes the sentence correctly. Then write the word in the space.

_____

- - - - - - - -

1. Mom's shed is _____.

    new   newer   newest

_____

- - - - - - - -

2. The lamp is _____ than the desk.

    old   older   oldest

_____

- - - - - - - -

3. This is the _____ path of all.

    long   longer   longest

_____

- - - - - - - -

4. My pup is _____ than your dog.

    small   smaller   smallest

McGraw-Hill School Division

Long *a: ai, ay*

Write a word from the box to complete each rhyme.

bait	gray	wait	tray

1. Hurry up. We already **ate.**
I can hardly

_____

- - - - - - - - - -

_____!

2. I went fishing with Nate.
The fish ate all our

_____

- - - - - - - - - -

_____!

3. It should be a sunny **day.**
Why is the sky cloudy and

_____

- - - - - - - - - -

_____?

4. "Oh, no!" yelled Fay. "I
tripped and dropped the

_____

- - - - - - - - - -

_____."

4 Book 1.4
Johnny Appleseed

At Home: Have children think of words that rhyme with
wait and **day,** and then make up a rhyme for each.

151

High-Frequency Words

Circle the word that completes each sentence.
Then write the word.

_____
- - - - - - - - -
how

1. This is a _____ pup.   little

_____
- - - - - - - - -
pretty

2. This is a _____ cat.   live

_____
- - - - - - - - -
live

3. They _____ here.   light

_____
- - - - - - - - -
pretty

4. This is _____   how
they go inside.

_____
- - - - - - - - -
little

5. They sit by the _____   light
of the fire.

At Home: Have children name the cat and pup and draw
another picture showing them both.

Gail the Train Nail

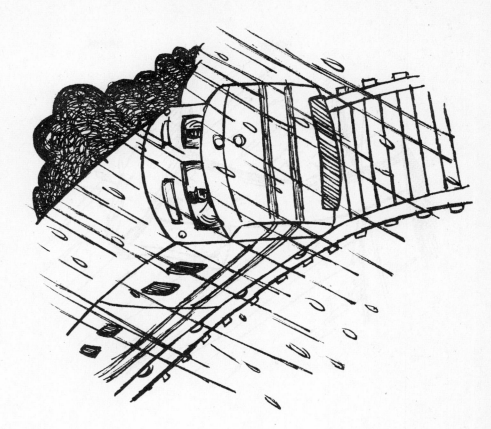

"How do you do?" said Gail to the man. "Can I stay on your train?"

"Can my light stay on you?" said the man.

"Yes!" said Gail.
And the nail was safe from the rain.

4

One day the rain came. Gail the little nail did not like rain. "I can not stay pretty in the rain," said Gail. "I do not have a place to live!"

Then a train came in the rain. The man in the train had a light. "I need light for my train to go. But there is no place for my light to stay."

Story Comprehension

Circle the pictures that tell what happened in "Johnny Appleseed."

1. Johnny Appleseed planted _____.

2. Johnny Appleseed sailed on a _____.

3. Johnny Appleseed slept with _____.

4. Johnny Appleseed had _____ as pets.

5. Johnny Appleseed ate at a _____.

6. Johnny Appleseed's _____ grew big.

A Chart

Look at this **chart** to see how a lemon tree grows.

Plant the Seed	Water the Seed	Let It Grow	Pick Lemons

Write the answer on the line.

1. What do you do first to grow a lemon tree?

_____

- -

_____

2. What do you do to help the tree grow?

_____

- -

_____

3. What grows on the tree before the lemons?

_____

- -

_____

4. What does the last part of the chart show?

_____

- -

_____

At Home: Have children make a tree or plant chart for a favorite kind of tree or plant.

Long *a: ay, ai*

Write a word from the box to complete each sentence.

way	May	wait	hail	train

1. I will _____ at the gate.

2. This is the _____ to the bus.

3. The icy _____ hit the truck.

4. The flowers came out in _____.

5. This is a fast _____.

5 Book 1.4
Johnny Appleseed

At Home: Help children to practice the long **a** sound by writing and drawing a picture for the following words: **play** and **trail**.

155

McGraw-Hill School Division

ai, ay; u-e, o-e

Draw a line from each sentence to the word that completes it. Then write the word in the blank.

_____
- - - - - - - -

1.  I eat my _____.

tune

_____
- - - - - - - -

2.  He plays a _____.

tail

_____
- - - - - - - -

3.  The shirt has a _____.

stain

_____
- - - - - - - -

4. The dog wags his _____.

clay

_____
- - - - - - - -

5.  She makes a vase with _____.

cone

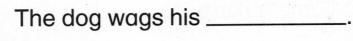

At Home: Have children write two questions using some of the words above.

Book 1.4
Johnny Appleseed

10

McGraw-Hill School Division

Make Inferences

Read the story. Then fill in the circles in front of the correct answers.

It was Saturday. It was time for Jack to clean his room. But Jack kept putting it off. Then, Joe came over to play. They went to the park. They played ball all day. When Jack came home, he ate a big dinner. Then he went to bed early.

1. Jack did not clean his room because he _____.

○ went to the park
○ read a book
○ walked his dog

2. When Jack came home from the park, he was _____.

○ excited   ○ sad   ○ hungry

3. Jack went to bed early because he was _____.

○ happy   ○ tired   ○ hungry

4. Did Jack like to clean his room?

○ yes   ○ no

McGraw-Hill School Division

4 Book 1.4
Johnny Appleseed

At Home: Have children predict what Jack will do about his messy room.

157

Inflectional Endings *-er, -est*

Add **-er** to compare two things.
Add **-est** to compare three or more things.

Read the word after each sentence. Then add **-er**
or **-est** and write the word to complete the
sentence.

1. Gail plays the game _____ _____
   than me.   fast

2. Kate's braid is the _____ of all.   thick

3. My train is _____ than
   yours.   long

Now draw a line from each sentence to the word
that completes it.

4. That is the _____ flag pole.   softest

5. This plum is _____ than that one.   fresher

6. Kate's bed is the _____ of all.   tallest

At Home: Work with children to illustrate one of these
sentences.

Book 1.4
Johnny Appleseed 6

McGraw-Hill School Division

ai, ay; u-e, o-e, i-e, a-e

Write a word from the box to complete each sentence.

fumes	smoke	spray	ride	rain

1. The fire made black _____.

2. They _____ water with a hose.

3. I want to _____ on a truck!

4. Do you smell the smoke _____?

5. The _____ put out the fire.

At Home: Have children draw a picture for the following words: **slide, hose, rule, sail,** and **day.**

High-Frequency Words

Write a word from the box to complete each
sentence. The pictures show what each sentence
means.

how	clean	always	work	done

I. I must _____ the rug.

2. This is _____ I do it.

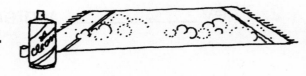

3. It is hard _____.

4. I _____ finish.

5. When I'm _____, I eat.

At Home: Have children draw a picture of something they
might clean at home.

Book 1.4
Ring! Ring! Ring! Put Out the Fire!

5

McGraw-Hill School Division

Hen and Snail

Snail went to Hen and asked for a bite to eat and a place to stay.

"From now on you must work." said Hen.

Snail said, "Yes." Hen and Snail became friends.

At Home: Have children talk about why work is important. What kinds of work are there? What kind of work do they like to do?

4

The red hen always got her work done.

"How clean my pen is!" Hen said.

But the snail did not want to work. She sat in the sun.

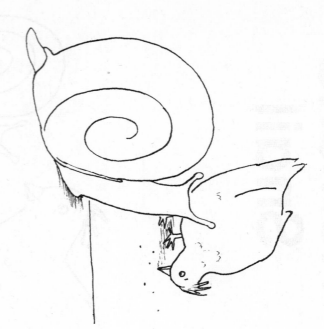

One day the hen went home to eat. The rain came. But the hen was safe.

The snail did not have a bite to eat. The snail did not have a place to stay.

Story Comprehension

Circle the sentences that tell what happened in "Ring! Ring! Ring! Put Out the Fire!"

1. The fire truck can rush to a fire.

2. The fire truck has things to put out a fire.

3. The fire hose can spray on a fire.

4. The fire truck is very small.

5. Masks help with smoke and fumes.

McGraw-Hill School Division

5 Book 1.4
Ring! Ring! Ring! Put Out the Fire

At Home: Have children draw a picture of items that firefighters use when they put out fires.

161

A Chart

Jon's class voted about where to go on a picnic. They chose from four places. This **chart** tells you how many votes each place got.

Place	Number of Votes
Mill Pond Park	I I I I I I I I I
Fish Creek	I I I I I I I
Sand Beach	I I I I I
Stone Hills	I I I I I I

1. How many votes did Fish Creek get? _____

2. How many votes did Stone Hills get? _____

3. Which place got the most votes? _____

4. Which place got the least votes? _____

At Home: Ask children to add the total number of votes to determine how many students were in the class.

Book 1.4
Ring! Ring! Ring! Put Out the Fire!

4

McGraw-Hill School Division

Cause and Effect

Read the question. Look at the picture. Underline the answer.

Effect	Cause

1. Why did the milk spill?

The cup was too full.
The knight bumped the cup.
The cup was too tall.

2. Why did the queen go away?

No one was home.
The king said to go away.
The prince was late.

3. Why did the queen call the knight?

He tells good stories.
She wants the dragon to go away.
The king is missing.

4. Why did the cook run in?

He saw a mouse.
The food was not cooked.
The pot was running over.

McGraw-Hill School Division

4 Book 1.4
Ring! Ring! Ring! Put Out the Fire!

At Home: Have children choose one of the effects and tell what happens next.

163

Make Inferences

Read the sentences. Circle the word that tells how the person might feel. Then write the word on the line.

1. Jill wants a new toy.
Her mom says no.
Jill is _____.

_____

sad   happy   excited

_____

2. Ann loves animals.
Dad brings her a hamster.
Ann is _____.

_____

sad   mad   happy

_____

3. Ray wants a snack.
He asks for an apple.
Ray is _____.

_____

silly   hungry   happy

_____

4. Dad looks at the clock.
He yawns.
Dad is _____.

_____

sad   happy   sleepy

_____

At Home: Have children cut out pictures of a person from a magazine and then tell something about the person.

Book 1.4
Ring! Ring! Ring! Put Out the Fire!

4

McGraw-Hill School Division

Inflectional Endings *-ed, -s, -es*

Add **-s** or **-es** to tell what one person or thing does **now**. Add **-ed** to tell what happened in the **past**.

Look at the underlined word in each sentence. Then look at the word after the sentence. Add **-s, -es,** or **-ed** to the underlined word and write the new word.

1. Dad braid Dale's hair.   past   _____

2. Lane grill the fish.   now   _____

3. Nash and I plant grapes.   past   _____

4. Gram wish for a soft quilt.   now   _____

5. Jen chain up her bike.   past   _____

6. Pat miss the bus.   now   _____

6 Book 1.4
Ring! Ring! Ring! Put Out the Fire!

At Home: Choose two sentences and act them out with children.

165

Inflectional Endings -er, -est

/Circle the word that completes each sentence.
Then write the word on the line.

1. Jan's hen is _____ of all.

   quick   quicker   quickest

2. His shed is _____ than mine.

   clean   cleaner   cleanest

3. Tom has the _____ legs in class.

   long   longer   longest

4. This box is _____ than that one.

   light   lighter   lightest

5. This is the _____ cake on the tray.

   plain   plainer   plainest

At Home: Ask children to illustrate the following words:
soft, softer, softest.

166

Book 1.4
Ring! Ring! Ring! Put Out the Fire!   5

McGraw-Hill School Division

High-Frequency Words Review

Circle the word that completes each sentence.

1. I see the ____ sky.

blue

ripe

2. Meg likes her ____ doll.

pretty

vote

3. The ____ boy ran fast.

cure

little

4. Kent wants to ____ this kite.

five

buy

5. My dog ____ his bone.

found

size

6. I see ____ smoke over there.

hive

some

7. The cat ran ____ away.

far

yoke

8. ____ many frogs are in the pond?

Pail

How

8 Book 1.4
High-Frequency Words Review

At Home: Have children write a sentence using one of the words they circled on this page.

167

High-Frequency Words Review

Write the word from the box that completes each
sentence.

| live   were   always   carry   who   light |

1. The mules _____ the packs.

2. I can see the _____.

3. Fish _____ in a tank.

4. They _____ play.

5. I know _____ it is?

6. We _____ there.

At Home: Have children make up a story about one of the
pictures on this page.

Book 1.4
High-Frequency Words Review

6

Long *e: ee*

Choose the word that completes the sentence.
Write the word.

feels	see	sheep	three	bee

1. Four is after _____.

2. I can _____ the cat.

3. He _____ happy.

4. The _____is in the hive.

5. The _____ are in the shed.

⑤ Book 1.5/Unit 1
Seven Sillies

At Home: Help children to practice the long **e** sound by making illustrations for the sentences on this page. Have them write each sentence under its picture.

High-Frequency Words

Write the word that completes each sentence.
Then circle the picture that the sentence describes.

four	all	many	so	over

1. I have so _____ cats!

2. The sheep jumps _____ the bush.

3. There are _____ hats.

4. We ate _____ the cake.

 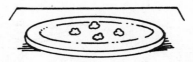

5. I was tired, _____ I went to sleep.

At Home: Have children write sentences using words from the box.

McGraw-Hill School Division

The Water Goat

The nice goat told the frog that the water goat never said a thing. "I've talked to the mean goat many times," said the nice goat.

So the frog jumped in the creek. The water goat went away. "The creek is free!" said the goat.

At Home: Ask children what they think the water goat really was. Then invite them to look at their own reflections in some water.

4

2

One day a nice goat looked in the creek. He saw another goat in the water.

The goat in the creek did not say a thing. So the nice goat thought the water goat was mean.

The nice goat went to the creek four times and saw the mean goat. The water goat still did not say anything at all.

One day a frog jumped over the creek.

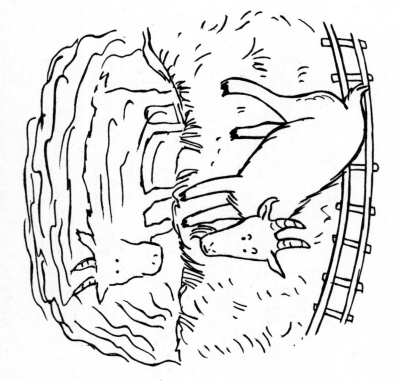

3

Story Comprehension

Write the names of the animals to complete the story.

Sheep   Pig   Goat   Rabbit   Hen   Mouse

One morning _____ looked into the

pond and saw a handsome animal. He called over

to _____, who saw a beautiful animal, and

he called over to _____ , who saw a

gorgeous animal. That animal called to the splendid

_____, who wanted _____ to come

and look. She called to dear little

_____. Then they all jumped into the

water. Frog laughed at them. He said they were

seven sillies. But there were really only six.

At Home: Invite children to continue the story by telling what happened after the animals laughed at Frog's mistake.

The Dictionary

A **dictionary** shows the meaning of words.
Read the meaning for each of these words.

rug   A rug is used to cover a floor.

sun   The sun is the brightest thing in the

   sky.

trail   A trail is a path.

Write the correct word to complete each sentence.

1. A _____ is a path.

2. The _____ is bright.

3. A _____ covers the floor.

4. You walk on a _____.

At Home: Ask children to look in a children's dictionary for
the definitions of three words.

172

Book 1.5/Unit 1
Seven Sillies   4

McGraw-Hill School Division

Long *e: e, ee*

First p**eel** the banana.   Then f**eed** it to the monkey.

Circle the word that answers the riddle. Then write
the word.

1. This looks like a snake
and swims in the sea.

_____

heel   eel   eagle

2. These grow all over.

_____

wheel   wide   weeds

3. Every bike has two.

_____

wheels   weed   steel

4. This will grow into a
plant.

_____

need   seal   seed

5. This is strong and hard.

_____

steep   seal   steel

6. This is the back of your
foot.

_____

heel   peel   feel

6   Book 1.5/Unit 1
    Seven Sillies

At Home: Have children think of other words that end like
peel and **feed**.

173

e, ee; ai

Sound out and say each word. Then write the word under the picture it describes.

she	bee	pail	sheep	chain

1.

_____

2.

_____

3.

_____

4.

_____

5.

_____

At Home: Have children think of other words that contain the letters **ee**.

McGraw-Hill School Division

Make Predictions

Circle the picture that shows what each person felt while playing a game.

1. John put his hand in the bag.
   He felt something long and thin.
   It was sharp at one end and soft at
   the other end. What did he feel?

2. Jan could feel something soft.
   It had two arms and two legs.
   What did she feel?

3. Sam could feel something
   round and smooth.
   What did he feel?

4. Pat could feel something with
   four wheels. What did she feel?

McGraw-Hill School Division

4   Book 1.5/Unit 1
Seven Sillies

At Home: Invite children to draw another picture to fit
with each group of sentences.

175

Inflectional Ending *-ing*

When you add **-ing** to a word that ends with a vowel and a consonant, double the final consonant.

Read each sentence. Then write the word that completes each sentence.

1. Ted was _____ with water.

   drip   dripping

2. The frog was _____ around.

   hopping   hop

3. Jane and Tom _____ rope.

   skipping   skip

4. Were you both _____ on the ice?

   slip   slipping

5. The kids _____ over the blocks.

   step   stepping

6. The girls are _____ the race.

   winning   win

At Home: Have children write another sentence using an -ing word.

Book 1.5/Unit 1
Seven Sillies   6

McGraw-Hill School Division

Long *e: ie, ea*

Write the word that completes each sentence.

field	neat	reach	real

I.

The rose is in a

_____

2.

Do you think it is

_____?

3.

I can _____

the top.

4.

Jumping with mom is

_____!

At Home: Help children to practice the long **e** sound by writing a sentence using the word **chief**, and another sentence using the word **steam**.

McGraw-Hill School Division

High-Frequency Words

Write the words from the box to finish the story.

before	off	our	right	come

1.

_____ with us, Max.

2.

Don't run _____ the path.

3.

We will get there _____ the sun sets.

4.

This is the _____ path.

5.

We are at _____ pond at last!

At Home: Have children write a story using one of the words from the box. Then have them draw pictures to go with their stories.

Book 1.5/Unit 1
Shrinking Mouse 5

McGraw-Hill School Division

The Fox

No, it is a frog. The dogs run after the frog. The frog gets away. The fox comes out of the field first. He is free.
I am glad.

At Home: Ask children why they think the speaker in this story is glad the fox will be free.

4

We hunt the fox in the field. We do not want him to eat our ducks. We do not want him to eat our chicks.

We put on our red coats. Our dogs run off before we do.

The Shrinking Mouse McGraw-Hill School Division

The dogs look for the fox. What is that? Is it a fox? No, it is a mouse. The dogs were not right.

The dogs try to find the fox. What is that? Did they find the fox?

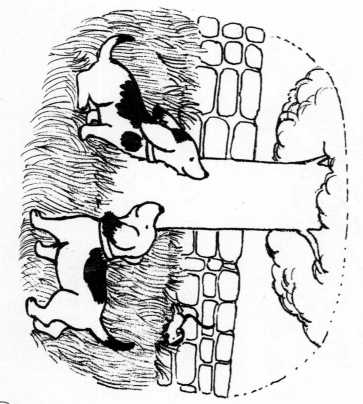

Story Comprehension

Think about the characters in "Shrinking Mouse."
Then draw lines connecting the names to their
pictures.

1. Fox

2. Squirrel

3. Mouse

4. Owl

5. Rabbit

At Home: Help children explain why these characters
kept following each other into the forest.

Read a Newsletter

A **newsletter** is like a short newspaper.
Write the correct words to answer each question.

Art Center News
May 12, 2001

New Art Materials
by Bob Pope

Good news!
The Art Center has new art materials.
Many new things came on Monday.
We have new crayons and new pencils.

We have new clay in bright colors.
We have new paper.
Now there are new paints and brushes. Come down and have some fun!

1. What did the art center get?

_____

2. When did they come?

_____

3. What were two things that came?

_____

_____

4. What does the newsletter say to do?

_____

At Home: Help children create a newsletter about a recent event at home or in the neighborhood.

180

Book 1.5/Unit 1
Shrinking Mouse 4

McGraw-Hill School Division

Long *e: ie, ea*

Choose the best word from the box to answer each riddle.

field	chief	reach	meal	leash

1. You plant seeds in me. What am I?

_____

2. You can eat me. What am I?

_____

3. You do this to get a thing. What am I?

_____

4. I am in charge. Who am I?

_____

5. Dogs wear me. What am I?

_____

McGraw-Hill School Division

At Home: Help children to write five sentences, each one using a word from the box.

ie, ea; e, ee

Write the words that make each sentence tell about
the picture.

1. He   Be   shield real

_____ has a _____.

2. stream queen   leaf beef

The _____ looks at a _____.

3. reach we   bee eat

Don't _____! Don't _____!

4. We Flea   bean team

_____ are the _____!

At Home: Have children write a new sentence using two of
the word choices not used on this page.

Book 1.5/Unit 1
Shrinking Mouse   4

McGraw-Hill School Division

Make Predictions

Look at the pictures. Fill in the circle in front of the
sentence that tells what will happen.

1.

○ The man will go on a trip.

○ There will be a party.

2.

○ The woman will put the plant on the table.

○ The woman will water the plant.

3.

○ Dad will take a nap.

○ Dad will get the ladder.

4.

○ She will go another way.

○ She will sit in the car.

4   Book 1.5/Unit 1
Shrinking Mouse

At Home: Have children draw a picture of their prediction
for one of the situations.

183

McGraw-Hill School Division

Inflectional Ending *-ing*

When you add -ing to a word that ends with a vowel and a consonant, double the final consonant.

Read each sentence. Then add -ing to the underlined word and write the complete sentence.

1. They are <u>step</u> on cracks.

_____

2. I am <u>trap</u> bugs.

_____

3. Mom is <u>chop</u> eggs.

_____

4. Grandpa is <u>sip</u> tea.

_____

5. I am <u>ship</u> a gift.

_____

At Home: Choose a sentence and work with children to write a short story using the sentence as a story starter.

Book 1.5/Unit 1
Shrinking Mouse   5

Long *o: o, oa, oe, ow*

Write the word from the box that names each picture.

| pillow | soap | hold | window | row | goes |

1.

_____

2.

_____

3.

_____

4.

_____

5.

_____

6.

_____

At Home: Help children to practice the long **o** sound by having them write four sentences using the following words: **soap, pillow, open,** and **goes.**

High-Frequency Words

Circle the word that completes each sentence.
Then write the word.

1.   kinds   high

We see many _____ of homes.

2.   more   by

The hive is made _____ bees.

3.   many   find

You can _____ a bear here.

4.   high   by

The nest is up _____.

5.   more   find

I see _____ hills.

At Home: Have children write the word **kinds** and draw
pictures of different kinds of homes in which animals live.

Book 1.5/Unit 1
You Can't Smell a Flower with Your Ear!   6

McGraw-Hill School Division

Pizza!

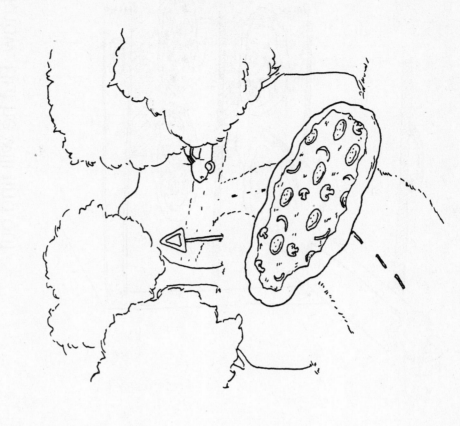

Mack closes the box. He knows why Pam can not eat pizza. The pizza is on the run! Mack wants no more pizza.

At Home: Invite children to make up a funny story about food, similar to this one.

4

186a

2

Mack wants to get pizza.
What kind does Pam like? Pam
cannot eat pizza.

Why is that? Mack does not
know. But he will find out.

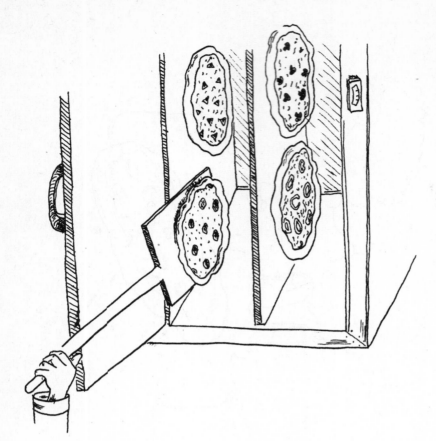

You Can't Smell a Flower with Your Ear! McGraw-Hill School Division

Max gets the pizza. He feels
the box shake. The pizza gets
out of the box. It flies high in
the air. It goes by Pam and
Mack. Then the pizza goes out
the door.

3

Story Comprehension

Think about "You Can't Smell a Flower with Your Ear." Then circle and write the right answers.

1. You see with your _____.

    eyes   ears

2. You hear with your _____.

    skin   ears

3. You feel with your _____.

    skin   eyes

4. You smell with your _____

    nose   tongue

5. You taste with your _____.

    ears   tongue

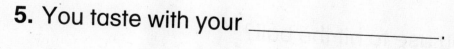

5 Book 1.5/Unit 1
You Can't Smell a Flower with Your Ear!

At Home: Have children talk about specific ways in which they use the five senses.

Use a List

A **list** can help you remember things.

What I Need for Baseball

1. baseball gloves
2. socks and shoes
3. shirt
4. pants
5. baseball bat
6. cap

rite the correct answer on the line.

Name two things you must have to play baseball.

_____

ame something you put on your head.

_____

are two things you put on your feet?

_____

you use to hit the ball?

_____

ren make a list of things that they need
y.

Long o: o, oa, oe, ow

Write the word from the box to complete each sentence.

slow	soap	mow	cold	toe

1. I wash with _____ .

2. Ice is _____ .

3. The bus was _____ .

4. Joe hurt his big _____ .

5. I _____ the grass.

5 Book 1.5/Unit 1
You Can't Smell a Flower with Your Ear!

At Home: Help children to practice the long **o** sound by writing sentences using the words: **show** and **float**.

189

o, oa, oe, ow; ie, ea

Circle the word that tells about the picture. Write
the word.

1.  cold

sold

_____

2.  beat

leaf

_____

3.  field

chief

_____

4.  toast

toad

_____

5. 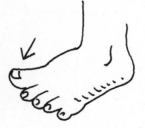 toe

hoe

_____

6.  slow

bowl

_____

At Home: Have children write sentences using the words
they circled.

Book 1.5/Unit 1
You Can't Smell a Flower with Your Ear! 6

McGraw-Hill School Division

Draw Conclusions

Read each story. Then underline the sentence that makes sense with each story.

1. Rita lives in a red house.

She drives a red car.

She likes to eat apples and cherries.

Rita has red hair.

She grows red roses.

Red is Rita's favorite color.

Rita lives in the city.

2. Ramona has a dog.

She has two cats.

She has a bird and some goldfish.

Ramona works at the zoo.

Ramona likes to read.

Ramona likes animals.

McGraw-Hill School Division

Context Clues

Context clues are words that tell you the meaning of another word.

Draw a line from the new word to the word or words that help tell its meaning.

1. pillow   what you think with

2. moment   quick time

3. sniff   a soft place for your head

4. bitter   breathe in

5. buds   little flowers

6. brain   not sweet

At Home: Work with children to choose two new words and write sentences that describe what the words mean.

Book 1.5/Unit 1
You Can't Smell a Flower with Your Ear! 6

McGraw-Hill School Division

Long *i: i, y, igh*

Circle the word that answers the riddle. Then write the word.

1. This is what you are.

_____

child   cry   crime

2. This warms the earth.

_____

sky   sunlight   sight

3. This is what you shouldn't do.

_____

light   fly   fight

4. This is what you use to think.

_____

mind   mild   mile

5. This is an insect with wings.

_____

fry   fight   fly

6. This is where you see the stars.

_____

sky   sight   sly

6   Book 1.5/Unit 1
Owl and the Moon

At Home: Encourage children to create their own riddles using the words on this page.

193

High-Frequency Words

Choose a word from the box to finish each sentence.

head	eyes	room	gone	everything

1. I see with my _____.

2. I sleep in this _____.

3. Where has the mouse

_____?

4. I pat my dog's

_____.

5. I put _____ on my

sandwich!

At Home: Have children make a diagram of their head that includes the labels **head** and **eyes** on it. Then help children label other parts of their face.

194

Book 1.5/Unit 1
Owl and the Moon

5

McGraw-Hill School Division

Owl in the Room

"Hoo! Hoo!"

"The owl is here for the night!" Ned said. "His bright eyes can be my light."

Everything was all right. The owl stayed the whole night.

At Home: Have children draw a picture that illustrates this story.

4

It was dark in the room. The light was out.

"There is an owl in my room," said Ned. "I can see the eyes and the head."

Ned's father said there was no owl in the room.

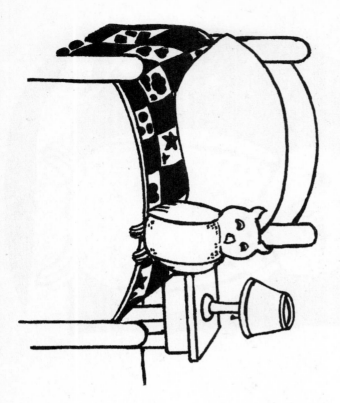

Ned saw the owl go. But Ned said the owl might be back.

"Hoo! Hoo!"

What was that? The owl was not gone.

But Ned's father said everything was fine.

Story Comprehension

Circle the pictures that tell what happened in "Owl and the Moon."

1. Owl looked at the ___.

2. Owl went on a ___.

3. Moon went after ___.

4. Moon is behind the ___.

5. Owl went to ___.

 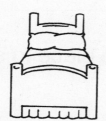

6. Moon shined in Owl's ___.

McGraw-Hill School Division.

Let's Read Signs

Signs can warn you about danger. Signs tell you where you can see a movie, buy things, eat dinner, or clean your clothes.

Fill in the correct answer on the line.

I. Where would you go to buy some fish to eat?

_____

2. How far is it to Dune River from the sign above?

_____

3. Which sign warns you about something?

_____

4. Which sign tells the name of a place to sleep?

_____

At Home: Have children make three signs for stores, streets, or other places in the neighborhood.

Book 1.5/Unit 1
Owl and the Moon   4

McGraw-Hill School Division

Long *i: i, y, igh*

Use the words in the box to answer the riddles.

right	night	sky	child	kind

1. I am not day. What am I? _____

2. The sun is here. What am I? _____

3. I am not left. What am I? _____

4. I am young. What am I? _____

5. I am not mean. What am I? _____

5   Book 1.5/Unit 1
Owl and the Moon

At Home: Help children to practice the long **i** sound by writing short stories that include the words **right** and **fly**.

197

i, y, igh; oa, oe, ow

Choose a word from the box to complete each sentence. Write the word on the line.

bright	fly	boat	hoe	throw	find

1. I _____ the ball.

2. The _____ is on the lake.

3. The birds _____ home.

4. The sun is _____.

5. I can not _____ my sock.

6. We use a _____ in the dirt.

At Home: Have children make up new sentences using some of the words above.

Book 1.5/Unit 1
Owl and the Moon 6

McGraw-Hill School Division

Draw Conclusions

Read the story. Then draw a line to finish each sentence.

Antonio went to visit Grandma and Grandpa. He flew on an airplane. Antonio took his special toy bear, Pete, to the airport.

Antonio does not know where Pete is. One day a box comes for Antonio. Antonio opens the box. Antonio is happy.

1. Antonio was excited   he sees Pete.

2. Pete is a   because he was going to visit his grandparents.

3. Antonio was worried   toy bear.

4. When Antonio opens the box   because Pete was lost.

Context Clues

When you don't know what a word means, look at the words around it to help you figure out the word's meaning.

Write the word that best completes the sentence. The underlined words will help you.

1. My <u>letter began with</u> " _____ Grandpa."

    Deep   Dear

2. Our <u>father's sister</u> is my _____.

    aunt   pan

3. We <u>eat</u> _____ at <u>night</u>.

    lunch   supper

4. This <u>soft</u> _____ helps me <u>sleep</u>.

    pillow   bunny

5. The king <u>dug</u> a _____ <u>around his home</u>.

    hole   tree

At Home: Pantomime two of the sentences and challenge a family member to guess what they mean.

200

Book 1.5/Unit 1
Owl and the Moon

5

McGraw-Hill School Division

Long *e, o, i*

Write the word from the box that names each picture.

sleep	fly	field	toe	soap	pillow

1.

_____

2.

_____

3.

_____

4.

_____

5.

_____

6.

_____

At Home: Help children to review the long **e**, **o**, and **i** sounds by writing a short story that includes the words **eat**, **row** and **light**.

High-Frequency Words Review

Complete each sentence with words from the box.

many	find	all	come	kinds

1. I must _____ my dog.

2. There are _____ places to look.

3. I look in _____ the right spots.

4. What _____ of places would he hide in?

5. My dog will _____ to me!

At Home: Have children draw pictures of places where they might find a bird, a fish, and a mouse.

202

Book 1.5/Unit 1
The Night Animals
5

McGraw-Hill School Division

The Mouse Hop

Who is that? All kinds come to the mouse hop. But not this kind. It is the cat. He will try to come in. He can not get in.
But now the mouse hop is done!

At Home: Invite children to dance like different kinds of animals. How would a mouse dance? How would a frog dance?

4

Have you been to a mouse hop? You have to be very small to go. The frog can go. The pig cannot. The chick can go. The hen cannot. Many small ones find their way to the mouse hop.

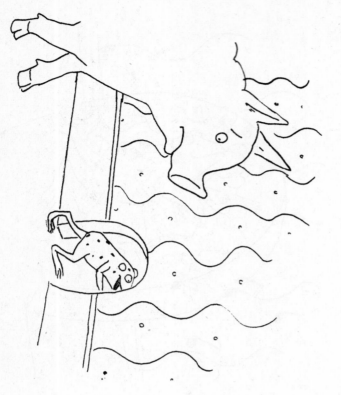

Rick Mouse and Pam Mouse spin their tails. Pete Frog jumps high with Kim Frog. There is cake and punch for all. They have a very good time. Then Rick hears a sniff.

Story Comprehension

Circle the sentences that tell about
"The Night Animals."

1. A bat eats bugs at night.

2. An owl hunts rats at night.

3. An owl can see and smell a rat.

4. Snakes like the hot sun.

5. Some pets stay up at night.

5   Book 1.5/Unit 1
The Night Animals

At Home: Have children write short stories about a night animal.

203

The Dictionary

A **dictionary** shows you what words mean.

A **bed** is something you sleep in.

When you **ride,** you sit on something and make it go.

If a thing is **wet** it has water on it.

Read the dictionary words on this page.
Complete each sentence with the correct word.

1. A **bed** is something you _____ in.

2. In a dictionary, does the word **wet** come before or after the word **train**?

   _____

3. You can _____ a bike or a horse.

4. The word _____ means **not dry**.

At Home: Have children look up the words on this page in a children's dictionary. Then ask them to draw a picture of someone riding a horse or bicycle.

Book 1.5/Unit 1
The Night Animals   4

McGraw-Hill School Division

Make Predictions

Write what you think will happen.

1. Lin wants to make a bed for her new puppy.
   What will she use?
   Lin will use a box.
   Lin cannot find a box.
   What will she use now?

_____

_____

2. It is Grandpa's birthday. What will Toby
   give him for a present?
   Toby will buy Grandpa a book.
   Toby cannot get to the store.
   What will Toby do now?

_____

_____

At Home: Have children write a few more sentences for
each story.

Draw Conclusions

Read the clues. Then draw a line to the correct
picture.

1. I swim in the water.
   You can cook me in a
   pan or a grill.

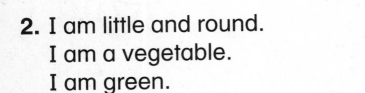

2. I am little and round.
   I am a vegetable.
   I am green.

3. I am long and orange.
   I grow under the ground.
   You can eat me cooked or raw.

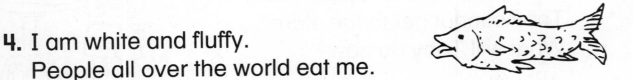

4. I am white and fluffy.
   People all over the world eat me.

5. I can be made from different
   kinds of greens.
   I can have tomatoes and lettuce.

Book 1.5/Unit 1   5
The Night Animals

McGraw-Hill School Division

Inflectional Ending *-ing*

When you add **-ing** to a word that ends with a vowel and a consonant, double the final consonant.

Write the word that completes each sentence.

1. Bill and Dan were _____wood.

   chop   chopping

2. The game is _____.

   begin   beginning

3. What will Nick and Sue _____?

   eat   eating

4. I keep _____ on my laces.

   trip   tripping

5. Jane's frog is _____ the game.

   win   winning

5 Book 1.5/Unit 1
The Night Animals

At Home: Have children write another sentence using an -ing word.

207

Context Clues

When you don't know what a word means, look for **context clues** in the sentence to help you figure out the word's meaning.

Draw a line from the new word to the clue that helps tell its meaning.

1. splendid   got small

2. fetch   land near the beach

3. shrunk   very wonderful

4. seashore   go get

5. vase   in back of

6. behind   a pot that holds flowers

McGraw-Hill School Division

High-Frequency Words Review

Write the word that completes each sentence.

1. The hat is not on her _____ .

   head   stop

2. The frog jumps _____ the rock.

   under   over

3. Don't make a _____ turn.

   rabbit   right

4. What _____ of fruit is this?

   kind   cakes

5. We get _____ the bus here.

   off   hidden

6. There are _____ many bugs.

   sheep   so

6 Book 1.5/Unit 1
High-Frequency Words Review

At Home: Have children tell about an adventure using the words they wrote.

209

High-Frequency Words Review

Circle the word that belongs in the sentence.

1. That is a __ cliff.

high

jail

2. The food is all __ .

gone

when

3. We __ went to the park.

they

all

4. My __ is right here.

room

jumped

5. I need __ in the box.

after

everything

6. We saw two __ sheep.

more

wait

7. We made __ cakes.

many

ears

8. __ ride with us.

Come

Grow

McGraw-Hill School Division

/ü/ oo

sch**oo**l   m**oo**n

Circle the word that answers the riddle.

1. Thread is wrapped around this.

spoon   spool

2. You need this to eat soup.

soon   spoon

3. You can sit on this.

stool   spoon

4. You need this to fix things.

school   tool

5. You swim here on a hot day.

tool   pool

6. This animal looks as if it has a mask on.

raccoon afternoon

6   Book 1.5/Unit 2
A Friend for Little Bear

At Home: Have children choose other words that sound like **school** and **moon** and then make up their own riddles.

211

High-Frequency Words

Write the word from the box that completes each
sentence.

these	called	pulled	only	friend

1. Put _____ books on the shelf.

2. I _____ have one egg.

3. My dog _____ me down
the street.

4. Dad _____ on the phone.

5. I sent the card to my _____.

At Home: Invite children to use several of the
high-frequency words in a story about playing outside.

212

Book 1.5/Unit 2
A Friend for Little Bear 5

McGraw-Hill School Division

The Not Too Small Room

Mick said the room was too small for all these things. Stan said to take the cab and van out. Mick did this. Now the room was just right!

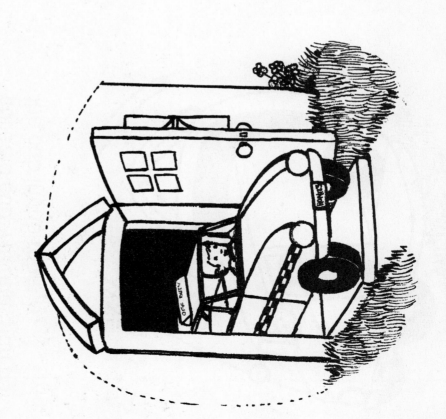

At Home: Invite children to talk about why the room in this story seemed small at first, then seemed just right.

4

212a

Mick had a home with only one room. He and his wife, Jan, lived there. They had a tot called Bob.

The home was too small. Mick did not know what to do.

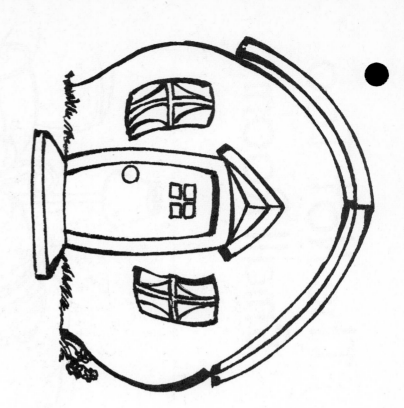

A Friend for Little Bear McGraw-Hill School Division

Stan was Mick's friend. Stan told Mick to pull a van into the room. Mick pulled the van into the room.

Stan said to call a cab. Mick called a cab. He and Stan put the cab in the room.

Story Comprehension

Think about "A Friend for Little Bear." Then draw a line to the words that best complete each sentence.

1. Little Bear lived by   things to play with.

2. He pulled out many   floated away.

3. The horse was   for a cup.

4. Little Bear looked and looked   the sea.

5. He piled his things in   to cry.

6. The horse fell off and   his friend.

7. Little Bear sat down   a heap.

8. He was glad when the horse   came back.

At Home: "A Friend for Little Bear" tells about the value of friendship. Ask children to explain why the horse was so important to Little Bear.

The Library

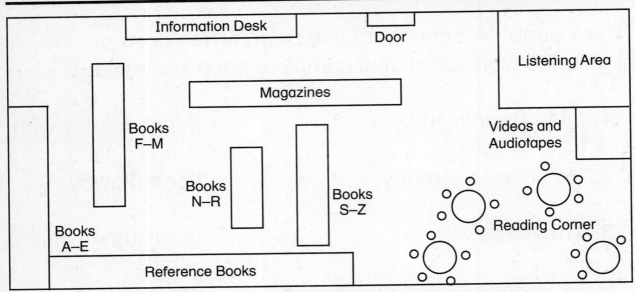

Look at the diagram to answer these questions.

1. Where would you sit to read a book?

_____

2. How many shelves of books are there? _____

3. Where would you find tapes to listen to?

_____

4. Where would you go to ask a question?

_____

5. Where would you find a book about **snow**?

_____

At Home: Go with children to your local library and show them where to find books and magazines.

Book 1.5/Unit 2
A Friend for Little Bear 4

McGraw-Hill School Division

/ü/ *oo*

We got out at n**oo**n today.

Read each word. Then unscramble the letters to make a word that rhymes. Write the word you make.

1. pool   l o t s o   _____

2. soon   p o n s o   _____

3. fool   l o t o   _____

4. bloom   zomo   _____

5. drool   p o l o s   _____

6. cool   oofl   _____

/ü/ *oo*; Long *e, o, a*

Circle the word that completes the sentence. Then
write the word in the blank.

1. I wash with _____.

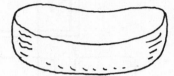

toast   moan   soap

2. We see snakes at the _____.

zoo   broom   boot

3. _____ likes to paint.

She   Be   See

4. The horse eats _____.

stay   hay   day

5. My bike needs a _____.

tree   heel   wheel

At Home: With children sound out each letter combined
with the long **e** sound to see if it triggers memories of any
words.

216

Book 1.5/Unit 2
A Friend for Little Bear   5

McGraw-Hill School Division

Fantasy and Reality

Read each sentence. Put an **X** under **Real** if the sentence tells something that could really happen. Put an **X** under **Make-Believe** if the sentence tells something that could not really happen.

	Real	**Make-Believe**
1. The cook made a big cake	____	____
2. Ted got a yellow hat.	____	____
3. The cat talked to the boy.	____	____
4. The goose sang a song.	____	____
5. The king wore a crown.	____	____
6. A cat rode a horse.	____	____
7. A man talked to the moon.	____	____
8. The girl cut the bug's hair.	____	____
9. The fish swam.	____	____
10. Mom fixed my pants.	____	____

McGraw-Hill School Division

10 Book 1.5/Unit 2
A Friend for Little Bear

At Home: Invite children to think of two more sentences, one that could really happen and one that could not.

217

Inflectional Ending *-ing*

Underline the word that completes each sentence.
Then write the word.

1. The sun is _____.

shine   shining

2. Papa is _____.

wave   waving

3. I _____ my horse.

ride   riding

4. Max is _____ bugs.

chase   chasing

5. I _____ the apple tree.

shake   shaking

6. Now I am _____ an apple.

bite   biting

At Home: Encourage children to write a story using one of the sentences on this page. Remind them that some words drop the final **-e** when **-ing** is added.

McGraw-Hill School Division

/är/ *ar*

There is a **m**a**r**k on my **c**a**r**.

Use one of the following words to complete each rhyme.

jar	bark	star	dark

1. "Please don't cry," said **Clark**.

   "There's nothing to fear.

   It's only the _____."

2. Can you tell me how near or **far**

   to travel to reach

   the nearest _____?

3. I once had a dog named **Spark**.

   When he saw the moon,

   he started to _____.

4. While unpacking the **car**,

   I dropped the bag

   and broke a _____.

McGraw-Hill School Division

4 Book 1.5/Unit 2
New Shoes for Silvia

At Home: Have children use pairs of words that rhyme
with **mark** or **car** to make up a rhyme.

219

High-Frequency Words

Draw a line from the sentence to the word that completes it.

1. The sun comes up in the _____.   once

2. Is it a big dog _____ a little dog?   or

3. Nell _____ a walk.   morning

4. There _____ was a little frog.   every

5. She walks home _____ day.   took

At Home: Write each high-frequency word on an index card. Shuffle the cards and have children choose words to read and use in sentences.

220

Book 1.5/Unit 2
New Shoes For Silvia 5

McGraw-Hill School Division

The Star

"Where am I?" said the star. "Am I far from home? Or am I close?"

She looked around. She was on a barn! High in the sky was Mars. "Thank you, Mars!" she said. "This is a good start!" The star was happy.

4

At Home: Have children draw a picture that illustrates this story.

Once there was a star. The star wanted a car. Every morning she would see if a car was there.

"Why do you want a car?" said Mars.

"I want to go far," said the star.

New Shoes for Silvia McGraw-Hill School Division

Mars took out a jar. "I do not have a car," said Mars. "But I have this."

The star got in the jar. Mars threw the jar very far. Crash!

Story Comprehension

Read the sentences. Underline the answers that tell about the story.

1. What does Tía Rosita send Silvia?

  a book   new shoes   a doll

2. What color are the new shoes?

  blue   black   red

3. The shoes are not right for Silvia. They are _____.

  too big   too small

4. Silvia uses the shoes to _____.

  make doll beds   hold candy   carry crayons

5. Silvia uses the shoes to make a _____.

  basket   two-car train   umbrella

6. Where does Silvia wear her new shoes?

  the post office   the school   the store

6 Book 1.5/Unit 2
New Shoes for Silvia

At Home: Have children draw pictures to show what happened in the story.

221

The Library

Look at the diagram. Write the word that best completes each sentence.

1. The _____ is someone who can help you at the library.

2. You can check books out and return them at the _____.

3. The librarian uses a _____ on the counter of the desk to check out books.

4. The _____ will also give you information.

At Home: Bring children to a library and show them how to check out and return books.

Book 1.5/Unit 2
New Shoes for Silvia   4

/är/ *ar*

shark

The word that names each picture has the same sound you hear at the beginning of **Ar**t. Circle the word and write it on the line.

1.

   tar
   bat
   jar

   _____

2.

   arm
   farm
   car

   _____

3.

   tart
   cart
   pair

   _____

4.

   car
   cat
   far

   _____

5.

   shark
   park
   show

   _____

5 Book 1.5/Unit 2
New Shoes for Silvia

At Home: Ask children to use each word that they wrote in a sentence.

223

/är/ *ar*; /ü/ *oo*; Long *i*, *a*

Fill in the sentences with the words in the box.

moon	try	may	bright	mail	jar

1. I _____ a letter.

2. The sun is _____.

3. Mick sees the _____ in the sky.

4. Little birds _____ to fly.

5. The jam is in the _____.

6. Please, _____ I have some milk?

At Home: Have children write a sentence using two of the words above.

224

Book 1.5/Unit 2
New Shoes for Silvia
6

Fantasy and Reality

Write **yes** or **no** to answer each question.

1. Can a  write a letter? _____

2. Can a lay an egg? _____

3. Can a  fly? _____

4. Can you bake a cake in the  ? _____

5. Can a  carry a baby in her pocket? _____

6. Can a  jump? _____

6 Book 1.5/Unit 2
New Shoes for Silvia

At Home: Have children tell about something real and
about something that is make-believe.

225

Inflectional Ending *-ing*

Add **-ing** to each pair of words. Then choose the correct word to complete each sentence. Write the word on the line.

1. drip   shade   _____

The jam was _____ .

2. slip   save   _____

I started _____ money.

3. take   skip   _____

Kim liked _____ dolls to the park.

4. wave   run   _____

Steve was _____ after me.

5. beg   gaze   _____

I kept _____ at the clock.

6. pet   joke   _____

Gail was _____ the kitten.

McGraw-Hill School Division

At Home: Have children write sentences for the words they did not already use.

/ûr/ *ir, ur, er*

Use these words to answer the riddles.

fur	her	bird	first

1. I can fly. What am I? _____

2. I come before everything else. What am I? _____

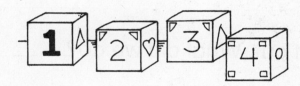

3. Cats and dogs have me. What am I? _____

4. I am not an "it." What am I? _____

At Home: Challenge children to think of a few more words that have the **/ûr/** sound in them.

High-Frequency Words _____

| sister | from | mother | walked | brother |

Write the word that best completes each sentence.

1. I have children. Who am I? _____

2. I am a girl. Who am I? _____

3. I am a boy. Who am I? _____

4. My dog and I went out. What did we do? _____

5. I tell you who sent the letter. What word am I? _____

At Home: Invite children to write and illustrate a sentence that includes two of the high-frequency words.

McGraw-Hill School Division

Pam's Surprise

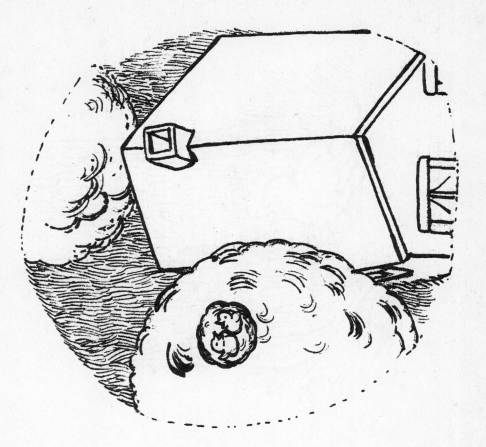

One day Pam took the bird out. There were many birds by the tree. The small bird walked to them. The big flock began to fly away from Pam. The small bird flew with them. Pam was sure the bird would be fine.

At Home: Ask the children about the main ideas in this story: Why couldn't the bird fly? What did Pam do? Why did the bird leave? How do you think Pam felt when the bird left?

4

One day Pam had a surprise. She saw a small bird fall from a tree. The bird could not fly. All the other birds had gone away. Pam took the bird home.

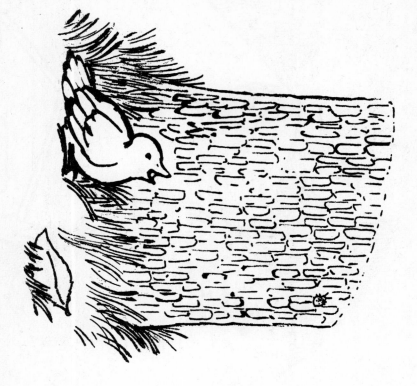

Pam walked in with the bird. Her mother, brother, and sister came to see it. Pam said she could look after the bird.

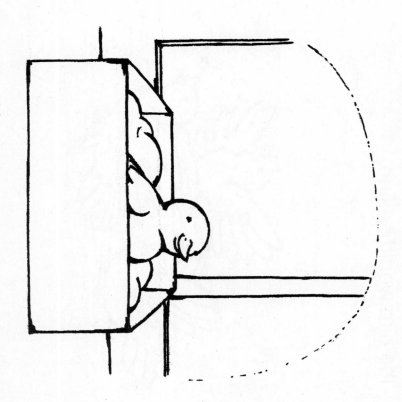

3

Story Comprehension

Think about "The Story of a Blue Bird." Then read each sentence. Circle **true** if the sentence happened in the story. Circle **false** if it did not.

1. The little blue bird was born in a nest.   true   false

2. His mother said there was nothing to see.   true   false

3. He walked away from his tree.   true   false

4. The little blue bird met a rabbit.   true   false

6. He wondered what nothing looked like.   true   false

7. He saw a pool of blue water.   true   false

8. The little bird went for a swim.   true   false

9. A green bird made him want to fly.   true   false

10. The little bird flew back home.   true   false

10 Book 1.5/Unit 2
The Story of a Blue Bird

At Home: Invite children to illustrate their favorite scenes from the story.

229

The Computer

The **library computer** can tell you where to find a book. *Title* tells you the name of a book. *Author* tells you who wrote the book. *Subject* tells you what the book is about.

Title:
<u>The Big Bad Bear</u>
by Sam Mack

Author:
<u>Sam Mack</u>
The Big Bad Bear
Dan's Fun Day
Gail Goes to the Fair
The Little Mouse

Subject:
<u>Bears</u>
Bears in the Wild
My Best Bear
The Big Bad Bear
Black and Brown Bears

Write the answer on the line.

1. Who wrote The Big Bad Bear?

_____

2. What other books did Sam Mack write?

_____

_____

3. On which screen would you find many books about bears?

_____

4. Would you use the title, author, or subject screen to find books by Jim Vine?

_____

At Home: Bring children to the library and help them use the computer to find books by title, author, and subject.

Book 1.5/Unit 2
The Story of a Blue Bird   4

/ûr/ *ir, ur, er*

Sound out each word. Write the word on the line.
Then circle the picture it names.

1. f e r n _____

2. s t i r _____

3. b u r n _____

4. h e r d _____

4 Book 1.5/Unit 2
The Story of a Blue Bird

At Home: Help children to list familiar words that contain the spellings **ir**, **er**, and **ur**.

231

/ûr/ *ir, ur, er;* /är/ *ar*

Write in the letters from the box to complete each word.
You can use each spelling more than once.

ir	ur	er	ar

1. st_____

2. y_____n

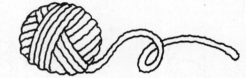

3. sk_____t

4. c_____l

5. f_____st

6. h_____d

Book 1.5/Unit 2   6
The Story of a Bluebird

McGraw-Hill School Division

Summarize

Read each story. Then write one sentence that tells what the story is about.

1. A frog lived in the pond. He did not like it when the ducklings went swimming. They would splash him and make noise. He would croak at them. One duckling told him to hop on her back. The duckling gave the frog a ride. The frog had fun. After that, he played with the ducklings when they came to the pond.

_____

_____

2. All of Fuzzy Duckling's brothers and sisters could quack. Fuzzy Duckling could not. She tried and tried. One day her brother said, "Boo!" Fuzzy Duckling jumped and said, "Quack." Then everyone laughed. Fuzzy Duckling was happy.

_____

At Home: Invite children to give summaries of their favorite stories.

233

Compound Words

A **compound word** is made up of two smaller words.

A. Connect the words to form compound words. Then write each compound word.

1. back   boat   _____

2. sail   room   _____

3. bird   pack   _____

4. sun   plane   _____

5. class   shine   _____

6. air   seed   _____

B. Use two of the new compound words in a sentence.

7. _____

_____

8. _____

_____

At Home: Invite children to write a sentence for the four compound words on this page that they did not use.

McGraw-Hill School Division

/ou/ *ou, ow;* /oi/ *oi, oy*

Use these words to answer the riddles.

soil	toy	down	boy	out

1. I am not up. What am I? _____

2. A seed is put in me. What am I? _____

3. I like to be played with. What am I? _____

4. I am not in. Where am I? _____

5. A man starts out as this. What am I? _____

At Home: Invite children to invent riddles for each of these words: **howl, shout, joy,** and **oil**.

235

High-Frequency Words

people	father	should	woman	horse

Write the word that fits best in each sentence.

1. The _____ likes grass.

2. No _____ live in the house.

3. The _____ made a clay pot.

4. We _____ write neatly.

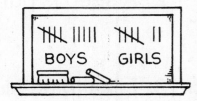

5. Ben's _____ flies an
airplane.

At Home: Play a pantomime game with children. Take turns
acting out high-frequency words for other players to guess.

Book 1.5/Unit 2
Young Amelia Earhart 5

McGraw-Hill School Division

The Old Horse

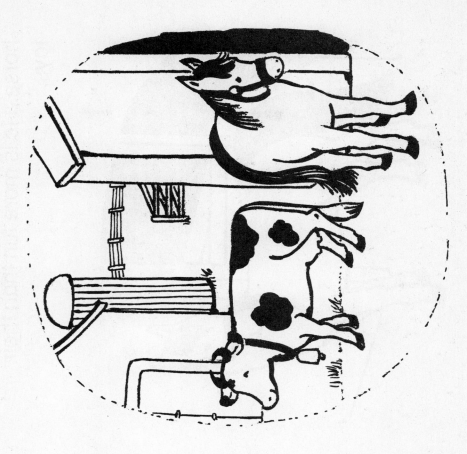

"What about your cow?" said the boys.

"I got her a dog!" says the woman.

Now the horse, the cow, and all the people are happy.

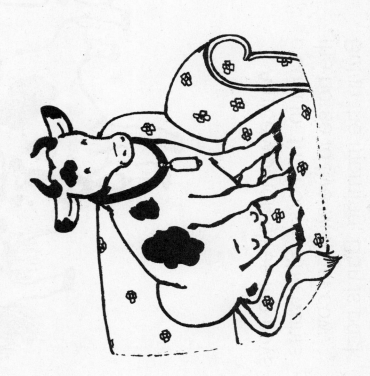

At Home: Invite children to talk about their pets, or an animal they would like to have as a pet. Why is that animal special?

4

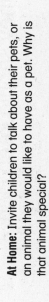

Father tells his boys to give away Dan the horse. Dan is old. Father wants a new horse.

The boys do not want to take Dan away. They will miss their horse. He is more fun than their toys.

A nice woman gives the boys a coin for the horse. She wants the horse to live with her cow. But in the morning, Dan is back with the boys. The woman says they should keep Dan.

Story Comprehension

Think about, "Young Amelia Earhart." Then answer the questions.

1. Where did Amelia Earhart live? _____

_____

2. What did she like to do when she was a girl?

_____

3. What did she see at the fair?

_____

4. What did she do after that?

_____

4   Book 1.5/Unit 2
Young Amelia Earhart

At Home: Invite children to draw a picture to accompany one of their answers.

237

McGraw-Hill School Division

A Glossary

A **glossary** tells the meaning of words in a book.
A glossary is found at the end of a book and lists
words in A-B-C order.

> **hen** A **hen** is a female bird.
>
> **home** A **home** is a place where someone lives.
>
> **hose** A **hose** is a tube used to move water.
>
> **hut** A **hut** is a small house or cabin.

Write the answer to each question on the line.

1. What is a hut?

_____

2. What is a hen?

_____

3. What word means a "tube to move water"?

_____

4. What word means "a place where someone lives"?

_____

At Home: Have children create two glossary entries for
familiar words. Help them look up the definitions.

Book 1.5/Unit 2
Young Amelia Earhart 4

McGraw-Hill School Division

/ou/ *ou, ow;* /oi/ *oi, oy*

Choose the word that completes the sentence.
Write the word.

how	cow	boil	coin	crown	snout

1. Hot water can _____.

2. The pig's _____ was big.

3. I know _____ to fly.

4. The king put on his _____.

5. I have a _____ in my pocket.

6. Our _____ gives us milk.

At Home: Ask children to make up rhyming sentences using **cow** and **now**; **oil** and **soil**; **toy** and **joy**; **about** and **shout**.

/ou/ ow, ou; /oi/ oi, oy; /ûr/ ir, ur, er

Sound out and say each word.
Then write the word under the picture it describes.

couch	stir	toy	hurt	crown	boil

1.

_____

2.

_____

3.

_____

4.

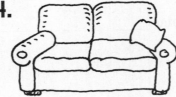

_____

5.

_____

6.

_____

At Home: Have children use the words they wrote in sentences.

Book 1.5/Unit 2
Young Amelia Earhart 6

McGraw-Hill School Division

Summarize

Read the story. Underline the answer to the question.

Today is Mother's birthday.
Will and Jill have a surprise for Mother.
Will picks flowers.
Jill makes toast.
Jill pours the juice.
Will carries the tray to Mother's bed.
Will and Jill say, "Happy Birthday, Mother."

1. Whose birthday is it?
   Bill's   Jill's   Mother's

2. Who picks the flowers?
   Mother   Will   Bill

3. What does Jill make?
   toast   eggs   tea

4. Where is Mother?
   outside   in the kitchen   in bed

5. How does Mother feel?
   sad   happy   sick

5 Book 1.5/Unit 2
Young Amelia Earhart

At Home: Have children tell a story about a birthday
surprise for a family member.

241

Compound Words

A **compound word** is made up of two smaller words.

Connect the words to form compound words. Write each new word on the line.

1. run   room   _____

2. out   day   _____

3. bed   side   _____

4. birth   way   _____

Now use the compound words above to complete the following sentences.

5. Let's go _____.

6. The plane was on the _____.

7. I sleep in my _____.

8. Today is my _____ .

At Home: Help children to make a list of some other compound words.

McGraw-Hill School Division

oo, ar, ir, ur, er, ow, ou, oi, oy

Circle the word that names each picture.
Then write the word on the line

1. fur purr _____

2. round down _____

3. food room _____

4. oil spoil _____

5. car star _____

6. thirst bird _____

7. her fern _____

8. boy toy _____

9. sour cloud _____

10. brooms boots _____

10 Book 1.5/Unit2
On the Go!

At Home: Ask children to make up a sentence that
includes both word choices.

243

High-Frequency Words

Read the sentences. Circle the word that completes each sentence. The write the word in the sentence.

1. I walked home _____ school today.

    or   from

2. My brother knows how to ride _____.

    pulled   horses

3. Do you want pizza _____ a salad?

    or   only

4. What kind of plants are _____?

    took   these

5. There were so many _____ on the airplane!

    people   called

At Home: Invite children to make up rhymes using the words they circled.

Horse Story

Some horses still stay far away from people. They like to live alone where there is room to play. They like to run in the hills!

At Home: Invite children to talk about other kinds of animals that were once wild but now are tame.

4

Horses have been around a long time. At first horses were only as big as large cats. Over time, horses grew. People soon put them to work.

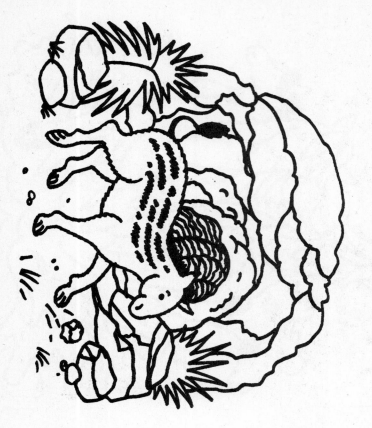

On the Go! McGraw-Hill School Division

Now, there are horses who can do tricks. They can jump and dance. Some can march or even play games.

Story Comprehension

Write each picture name under the box where you might see it. Then draw a picture of it.

| boat | train | ship | car | plane |

_____

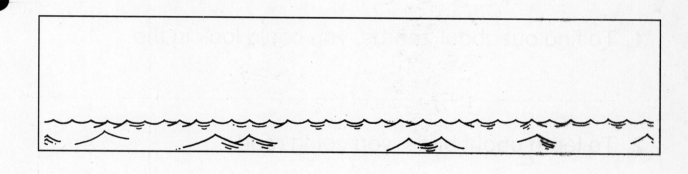

_____   _____

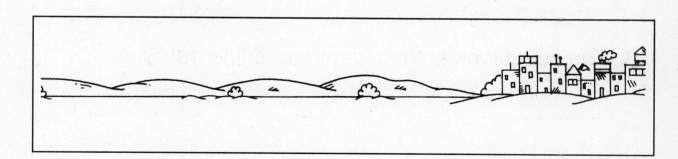

_____   _____

At Home: Invite children to make posters showing the kinds of transportation they have used.

Information Resources

You can find **information** in books, videotapes, encyclopedias, and audio cassettes.
You can find all of these at the library.

Choose one of the resources pictured above to complete each sentence.

1. To find out about zebras, you could look in the

_____.

2. To learn about birds, you could read

_____.

3. You could look at the videotape to find out how

_____.

4. "Bedtime Songs" is an _____.

At Home: Have children think of a subject they would like to learn more about. Then go to the library and work together to find sources of information about the subject.

246

Book 1.5/Unit 2
On the Go! 4

McGraw-Hill School Division

Fantasy and Reality

Read the story. Then write an **X** next to the sentences that tell about **make-believe** things.

1. _____ I went to school on Monday.

2. _____ I met a space girl.

3. _____ I read a good book at school.

4. _____ I took a test.

5. _____ A tiger gave the test.

6. _____ I went home on a spaceship.

Summarize

Read each story. Write one sentence that tells what
the story is about.

Gus had a dog named Jake. Gus taught Jake to
do many tricks. A man saw Jake do his tricks. He
took Jake to the city. You can see Jake do tricks on
the man's show.

I. _____

_____

Jordan sent letters to every boy and girl in the
class. He brought balloons to school. Anna's
mother baked a cake. When the teacher came into
the room, everyone said, "Surprise!"

2. _____

_____

At Home: Have children give a one-sentence summary for a
story they know.

248

Book 1.5/Unit 2
On the Go! 2

McGraw-Hill School Division

Inflectional Ending *-ing*

Read each sentence. Write the word that completes the sentence.

1. We are _____ a trip.

    plan   planning

2. The kids are _____.

    skate   skating

3. The girls _____ the dress.

    pin   pinning

4. Nick is _____ the train.

    take   taking

5. We _____ good-bye.

    wave   waving

6. The farmers are _____.

    smile   smiling

McGraw-Hill School Division

At Home: Ask children to add several more sentences to this page that use the inflectional ending **-ing**.

Compound Words

A **compound word** is made up of two smaller words.

Draw a line between words to make a compound word.
Then write the compound word on the line.

1. in   ring   _____

2. ear   man   _____

3. snow   side   _____

4. bath   shell   _____

5. sea   tub   _____

Use the new compound words to answer the riddles below.

6. Wash yourself in me. What am I? _____.

7. I am not outside. What am I? _____.

8. Find me on the beach. What am I? _____.

9. Make me on a cold day. What am I? _____.

10. Wear me on your ear. What am I? _____.

At Home: Help children to use the words **snowstorm**, **carwash**, and **backdoor** in a sentence.

Book 1.5/Unit 2
On the Go! 10

McGraw-Hill School Division

Name_____ Date_____

High-Frequency Words Review

Circle the word that tells about the picture. Then write the word.

baby

mother

2. _____

friend

girls

3. _____

mail

morning

4. _____

sisters

brother

5. _____

wo

people

6. _____

people

At Home: Have children use each of the words they circled in a sentence.

McGraw-Hill School Division

Name_____ Date_____

High-Frequency Words Review

Circle the word that goes in the blank.

1. —, he was on time.

    Beach

    Once

2. I — the ro

    pulled

    some

3. She — my name.

    airplane

    called

4. — pants a

    Brave

    These

    ours.

5. We were hidden —
   him.

    from

    broke

6. I — the

    took

    nut

7. Jane hits the ball —
   time.

    every

    who

8. You can ha
   a cat.

    or

    king

High-Frequency W